D1058762

50

Things to See with a Small Telescope

John A. Read

www.facebook.com/50ThingstoSeewithaSmallTelescope

A note from the Author

When I look through my telescope, I am exploring a new and fantastic frontier.

Just like you, I want to skip to the middle of this book, pick something cool, and see it with my telescope. However, only about a third of the items in this book will be visible in a given evening. Before you set up your telescope, please download stargazing software for your computer or mobile device. I recommend Stellarium, which is available for free at http://www.stellarium.org, or from the app store. Using this software, you can determine if your target is visible.

Since I do my astronomy in the northern hemisphere, this edition of the book contains several items visible only to those living north of the equator. A Southern Hemisphere edition of this book is also available.

Finally, as the first of many reminders, do not look at the Sun, through a telescope, without utilizing a commercial solar filter.

Star maps used in this book are made using Stellarium, http://stellarium.org/ an open source stargazing program.
Cover photo by Sean McCauley.
Copy editing and final proof by Kurtis Anstey
Images of the following telescopes provided compliments of Celestron: Celestron First Scope and Celestron NexStar 6se
Images of the following telescopes reprinted with permission from Orion Telescopes & Binoculars: 6 Inch Orion SkyQuest, 8 Inch Orion SkyQuest
Image of Meade Lightbridge Dobsonian provided compliments of Meade Instruments
Image of Explore Scientific FirstLight 114mm Reflector provided by Explore Scientific
Telescope view source files for deep sky objects were constructed from actual astrophotos used with permission from the following astrophotographers:

Mark Stanford Sr: Trifid Nebula

Stuart Forman: Double Cluster, M1, M13, M27, M51, M81 & M82, M81 (Supernova added digitally).

Mike Harms: Andromeda, M42

Dave Lane (Utilizing the Burke-Gaffney Observatory): Comet Catalina

Images from NASA follow NASA's photo usage guidelines found here: http://www.nasa.gov/audience/formedia/features/MP_Photo_Guidelines.html
Solar and Lunar Eclipse Schedule based on data acquired by Fred Espenak during his time at NASA's Goddard Space Flight Center. Permissions freely granted based the guidelines found here: http://eclipse.gsfc.nasa.gov/SEpubs/5MCSE.html

This book is dedicated to Jennifer, who listens to me to talk about outer space pretty much all of the time.

Acknowledgments

I would like to express my gratitude to Marni Berendsen, developer of the NASA Night Sky Network, for her fantastic contribution of editing and fact-checking this book.

I would also like to thank the Mount Diablo Astronomical Society (MDAS), for feeding my desire to learn more about the universe. This book would not be possible without the support of the wonderful folks at MDAS.

To find the astronomy club nearest you, please visit:
http://nightsky.jpl.nasa.gov (USA)
www.rasc.ca/locations-across-canada (Canada)
www.skyandtelescope.com/astronomy-clubs-organizations/ (All)

Table of Contents

Introduction

I wrote this book to accompany a person's first telescope. It saddens me that many telescopes are used once, and then shoved to the back of a closet. I assume folks are persuaded to purchase these telescopes based on the pictures of planets and galaxies on the box, leading them to believe their new scope is as powerful as the Hubble Space Telescope. Or maybe it was a well-meant gift, lost to time.

Maybe you tried to use the telescope, but realized the mount was too flimsy, the optics were poor, or if it had a go-to computer, that computer didn't know Jupiter from the Moon.

My first three telescopes met these criteria. As a kid, I spent hours looking at random objects in space, dreaming I might someday see something cool. I desperately hoped to see something to ignite my soul, slingshotting me into a lucrative career as an astronaut or astronomer.

I was an adult before I had an enlightening experience with a telescope, and well into an established career in corporate finance, when my soul was truly ignited for astronomy. The local pharmacy was selling small telescopes for $13.99. The box was beautifully designed with pictures of Saturn and Jupiter. I thought, *what the heck, I'll do it, I'll buy this telescope!*

I carried the telescope home and set it up. "This is terrible!" I thought, feeling embarrassed for wasting my money. The telescope sat on a camera tripod instead of a proper telescope mount, the eyepieces were tiny, the aperture was the size of a silver dollar, and the finder scope was obviously just for decoration.

Testing my $14 telescope

That night I carried the telescope outside, setting it up in front of my apartment complex, under a streetlight and beside a Bay Area Rapid Transit station. I pointed the small telescope at a bright yellow star hovering a few degrees above the horizon.

"Oh, my," I thought, overwhelmed with awe. The wobbly scope steadied itself in the still air. Before my eyes, in perfect clarity, in perfect focus, without a shimmer of distortion, I saw, for the first time in my life, Saturn and its rings.

You may be wondering what inspired me to write this book? I do a lot of volunteering with my local astronomical society's outreach group, through NASA's Night Sky Network. We go from school to school teaching students how to use a telescope. The thing is, even though we are in California, the sky is not always clear, and this happens:

Kid: "Can we look at the Sun?"

Me: "No, you can only see the Sun during the day."

Kid: "Can I see the Moon?"

Me: "No, it's not up tonight. But there are other things to see."

Kid: "Like what?"

Meanwhile the clouds begin to roll in.

Me: "Like this!" I point the telescope at Saturn.

Kid: "I don't see it."

Me: "Ah, a cloud has strategically positioned itself in front of Saturn."

The kid walks away.

When this happens, it's time to get creative; otherwise, mayhem follows. The students start to get bored, and they start throwing things. The teachers give them flashlights, which they shine in your eyes. You turn your back for ten seconds and then there is a child riding your telescope like a horse.

Sometimes, we need to think unconventionally. I was on top of Mount Diablo, at an astronomy event, when the clouds rolled in. I decided to point the telescope at a red light on the top of the observation building at the summit. The students were fascinated!

The light was a quarter mile away, yet you could see the condensation on the red glass enclosure. A moth fluttered around it.

The kids noticed how the light bulb appeared upside down in the scope, and I had to explain how this was due to the lenses and mirrors inside. In looking at a light-bulb a quarter mile away, we were able to grasp the power of the telescope; the ability to see something familiar, small, and far away.

We spent half an hour looking at that light bulb. It was seen by at least a hundred people. That night probably churned out as many future scientists as a night where there were no clouds at all. I started thinking unconventionally about what to observe, and how to best share the observations; breaking down stargazing into its simplest form. And that's how *50 Things to See with a Small Telescope* began.

John Read speaking about astronomy outreach at the local astronomy club

Telescope Shopping

Since I published the first version of this book, back in 2013, many people have contacted me asking what telescope they should buy given their budget. The most common response to this is: it depends. I hate giving that response. Most people who are getting started in amateur astronomy have one goal: **to see cool stuff**. They're not trying to take pictures, make groundbreaking discoveries, or memorize the constellations. With this in mind, my one rule for a first telescope is to get the one with the most aperture you can afford (aperture is the diameter of the primary lens or mirror).

Celestron First Scope

If your budget is around $75: This table top scope has 76mm of aperture, more than enough to see everything in this book. And for around $50 (plus tax), you can't beat the easy to use table top mount.

Between $100 and $150: At this price range, start looking for telescopes with over 110mm (~4.5 inches) of aperture. This will enable great views of Saturn's rings, and hundreds of deep sky objects.

Explore Scientific FirstLight 114mm f/4.3 Reflector Telescope

6 Inch SkyQuest

Between $150 and $300: In this range, we're looking at some really great telescopes. Try your best to reach the six inches of aperture range, you won't regret it! Dobsonians make extremely loveable telescopes.

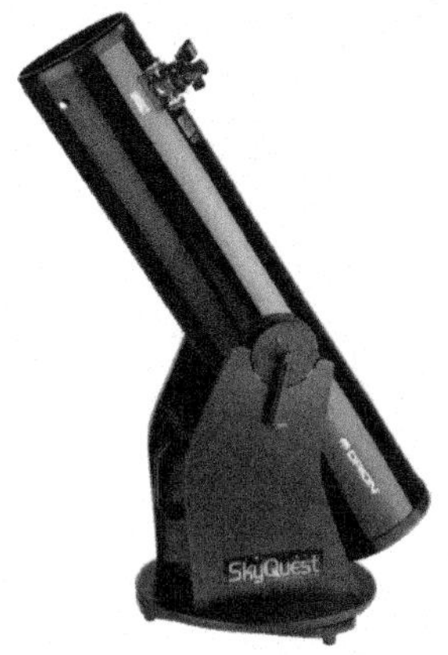

8 Inch Orion SkyQues Dobsoniant

Between $300 and $500: At this price range, we can move beyond the small telescope. These telescopes have between six and ten inches of aperture. Personally, I prefer Dobsonians for their ease of use, and spectacular views of galaxies, nebulae, and globular clusters. However, if the size of a Dobsonian is an issue, consider a Maksutov-Cassegrain telescope, instead.

Between $500 and $1000: A twelve inch Dobsonian is a serious telescope. In dark skies, you can see distant comets, and dim galaxies. Some people even use these telescopes to search for undiscovered supernovae! At this price range, you may want to consider trading aperture for a computerized telescope. Dollar for dollar, I prefer aperture to computing power, but it is an option.

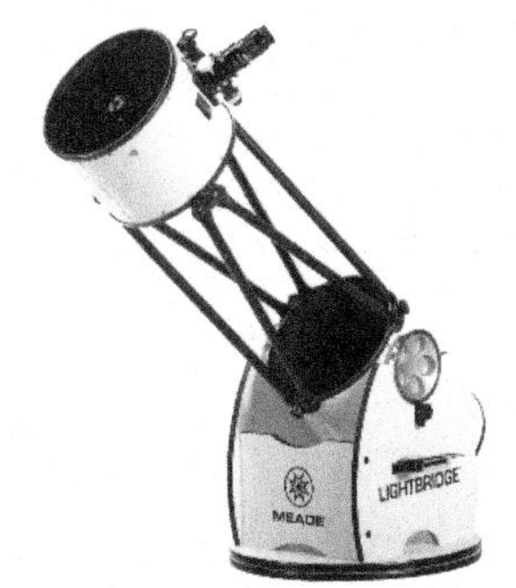

Meade Lightbridge Dobsonian

Celestron NexStar 6se

When priced under $1000, decent go-to (computerized) telescopes tend to have no more than six inches of aperture. However, many go-to scopes have great features like sky-tours and satellite tracking. Newer models, like the NextStar Evolution Series, have internal lithium ion batteries, and can be controlled by a phone or tablet.

A Note on Color

Did you know that in dim lighting the human eye can only see in black and white?

Only when you use a digital camera do galaxies and nebulae get color. Many objects imaged using professional telescopes aren't even in wavelengths the human eye can see! In this case, professional astronomers assign a color the human eye *can* see to that particular wavelength of light. This is called false color, or representative color.

This book is about what **you** can see through your telescope, not what a camera can image. Amateur astronomers often call deep-sky targets "beautiful smudges", because without a camera, that is what most deep-sky objects look like.

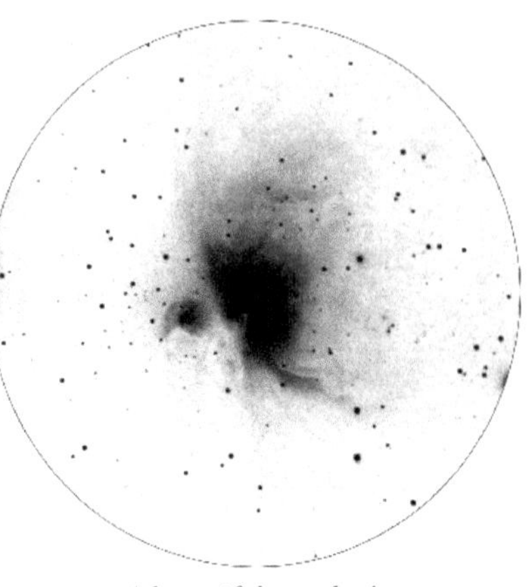

A beautiful smudge!

For this reason, this book is different than most other beginner astronomy books. All "telescope view" photos of galaxies and nebulae are in greyscale, to simulate how they will look through the eyepiece. I've also chosen to keep the paperback editions in black and white, which saves you, the budding astronomer, money that you can now put towards your new telescope!

Adapting Your Eyes to the Dark

Most of the items in this book, including stars, planets, and the Moon, can be seen with ease, if the telescope is pointed in the right direction. However, when you move on to section three, *Deep-Sky Objects*, you'll need to adapt your eyes to the dark, before attempting to observe.

How do you adapt your eyes? You prepare your eyes to view deep-sky objects by avoiding looking at any light source, for at least twenty or thirty minutes. This means avoiding looking toward porch lights, cell phones, and car headlights. It also means avoiding bright objects in the sky, including the Moon and planets, too.

What can you do while you wait? Besides watching for shooting stars, you can observe double stars, and star clusters like the Pleiades.

Stargazing Checklist

1. A telescope (or binoculars), and a couple eyepieces.

2. A basic understanding of how to focus your telescope, and point it at the bright stuff in the sky.

3. A dark, cloud-free sky (if you are viewing galaxies, nebulae, and globular clusters). To find the darkest skies near you, use this website: http://darksitefinder.com/maps/world.html

4. A stargazing application for determining the location of the planets.[1] I recommend "Stellarium" (it's free): http://www.stellarium.org.

5. A commercial solar filter, or Coronado PST. If you plan on using your telescope to look at the Sun, ALWAYS use a solar filter over the **objective lens** or **primary mirror**.[2]

[1] Planets do not follow any annual calendar, so you will need software to find a planet's current position in the sky.

[2] Never use a solar filter that covers only your eyepiece. The sunlight will burn through the filter and YOU WILL IMMEDIATELY GO BLIND.

Difficulty

☼	Seriously, how have you not seen this before?
☼☼	Probably one of the brightest objects in the sky
☼☼☼	If you can see this, you're officially an amateur astronomer!
☼☼☼☼	Astronomers envy your accomplishment*
☼☼☼☼☼	Challenging, and not for the faint of heart!

*Sometimes it can take hours of patience to finally find the object you are looking for, and it may not always be spectacular; but that's not the point. The point is to appreciate the objects that you can see! Hopefully, this book will help you appreciate the true splendor of everything in the sky.

Part One

Stars and Constellations

This section will focus on a several popular stars, constellations, and asterisms (patterns within constellations). Learning to locate these stars and star-patterns will familiarize you with the night sky, and help you locate the other objects mentioned in this book.

Each section will feature at least one star worth observing with your telescope. As you view the star, take note of its color. Is it orange, yellow, white, or blue? Is the star alone, or in a pair? Many people don't realize that stars come in several colors, or that they typically have companions. Simply viewing stars through your telescope, and learning to appreciate their beauty, is often one's first step into the larger Universe.

Long exposure photograph of the northern sky, with my refractor telescope in the foreground

1. The North Star (Polaris)

Many people have incorrect assumptions about which star is actually the North Star. Some people believe that it's the brightest star in the sky. I've actually had folks argue with me over which star is the North Star, some people even pointing to Sirius (located on the other side of the sky), just because it was the brightest star they could see at the time. In reality, the North Star is the 48th brightest star in the night sky.

To find the North Star, follow the two stars (often called the Pointer Stars) that form the front of the cup of the Big Dipper to the next brightest star (as shown in the diagram below).

The North Star is what is commonly called a visible binary star. With your telescope, you may be able to make out the second star, Polaris B.

Polaris is very important to folks who own an equatorially mounted telescope in the Northern Hemisphere. In order for this type of mount to function correctly, one axis must be pointed directly at this star.

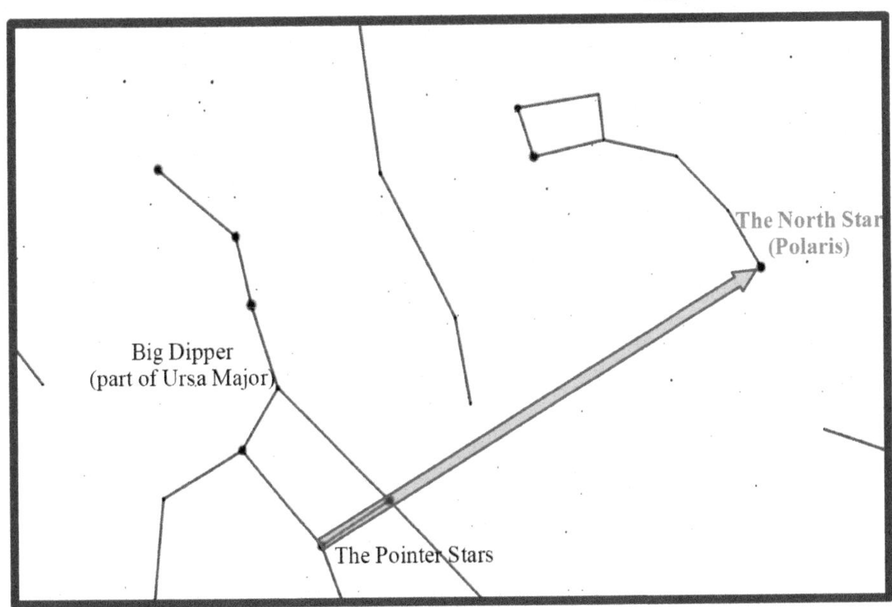

2. Arcturus and Spica

Beginning in the springtime, "Arc to Arcturus then Spike to Spica" is a great phrase to remember as you begin to navigate around the eastern sky. By creating an arc with the handle of the big dipper, and following it across the sky to arrive at the bright star Arcturus, you can then straighten your arc to hop over to the bluish star, Spica.

Arcturus is an Orange Giant, and the fourth brightest star in the sky. Spica is a Blue Giant, and the fifteenth brightest star. Spica resides in the constellation Virgo, while Arcturus is located in Boötes (which is much more fun to say).

Arcturus is very interesting, as over the course of our lifetime it will move, relative to nearby stars (about one seventh the diameter of the Moon, in one hundred years). The star is moving at over 90 miles per second, so fast that in 500,000 years it will be gone from sight altogether!

Spica is both rotating and variable (increases and decreases in brightness). At its equator, it rotates at almost 200 kilometers per hour, and changes in brightness ever so slightly with each rotation.

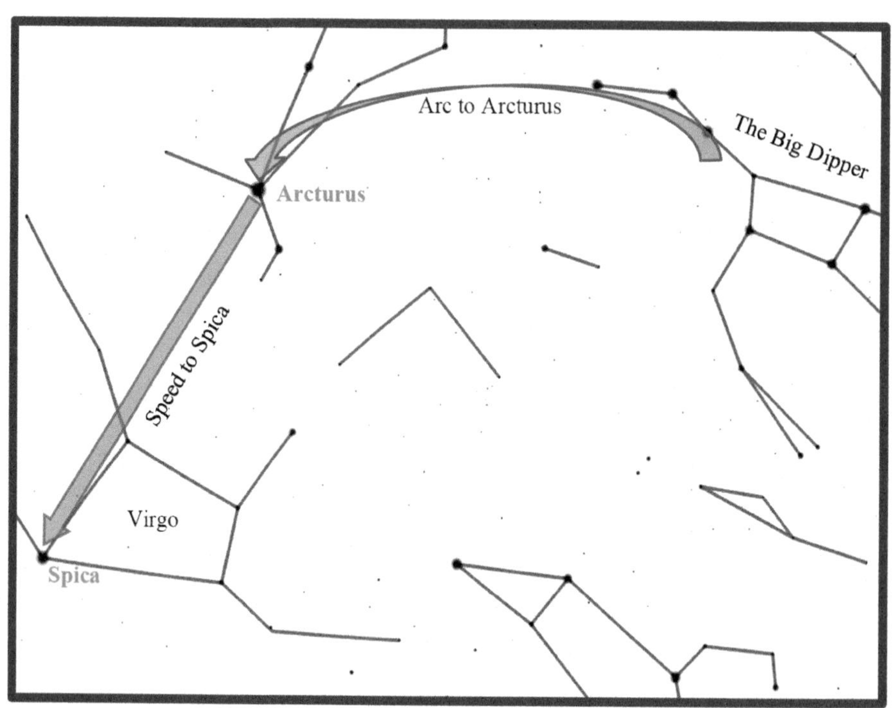

3. Altair & the Summer Triangle

Stars and Constellations

The Summer Triangle (or as my wife calls it, "The Great Pizza Slice") is an interesting part of the sky, as it straddles the plane of our galaxy. Because of this, it is filled with many objects to discover as you dive deeper into astronomy and upgrade to larger telescopes.

The Summer Triangle is a great way to learn your way around the sky. It is outlined by three stars: Vega, Deneb, and Altair. An asterism called The Northern Cross (in the constellation Cygnus) is also frequently referenced to locate targets in this part of the sky.

Altair is frequently mentioned in science fiction due to its proximity to Earth. At only 16.7 light years away, it is one of the closest bright stars. Altarian dollars is the currency used throughout *The Hitchhiker's Guide to the Galaxy*. Altair is also mentioned in multiple Star Trek episodes, *Star Trek, The Wrath of Khan*, and two episodes of *Doctor Who*.

No planets have been discovered orbiting Altair, but this may change in 2018 with the launch of a spacecraft called TESS (Transiting Exoplanet Survey Satellite). TESS will continually scan two million of the closest star systems, searching for Earth-like planets.

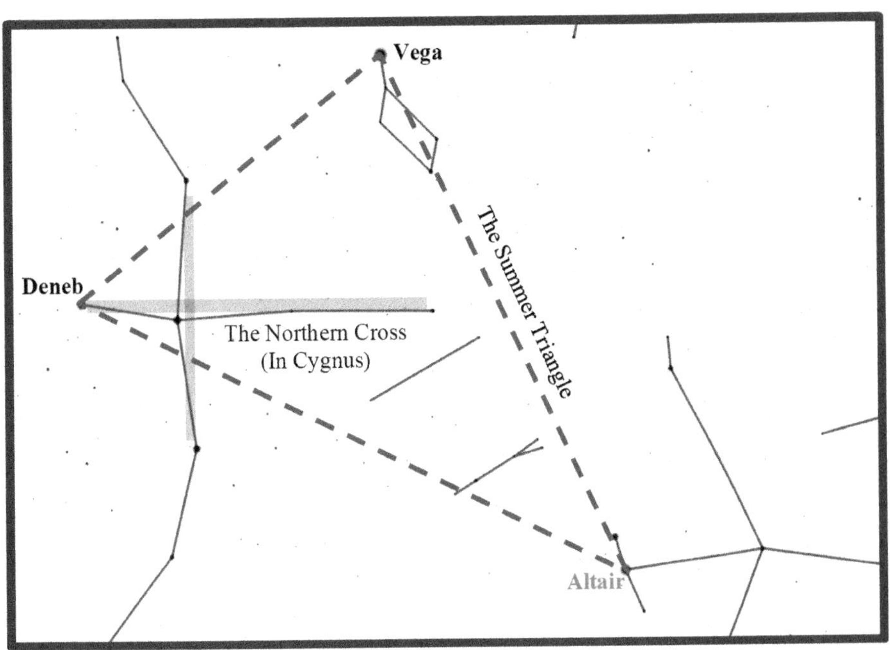

Difficulty: ☼

4: Pollux and Castor

The constellation Gemini rises near midnight in the autumn, and is at its best during the evenings in winter and spring. Gemini is visualized by picturing twins holding hands. Stars Castor and Pollux make up the heads of these twins.

The star Castor, the head of the rightmost twin, is a double star when viewed through a telescope. But Castor is a sextuple star system; six stars bound together by gravity. These six stars can only be separated by an extremely strong telescope, or through the science of spectroscopy (breaking down light into different wavelengths).

The star Pollux, the head of the leftmost twin, used to be a "main sequence star" like our Sun. However, it burned through its hydrogen, and has since expanded into a "giant" star many times the radius of our Sun. A surface temperature of just under 5000 degrees Celsius gives the star its orange color. Pollux is also the brightest known visible star with an orbiting planet, but this will change as new planets are discovered.

The Geminid meteor shower in mid-December is one of the most prolific meteor showers of the year. Be sure to give your eyes plenty of time to adapt to the dark, this way you'll see even more shooting stars.

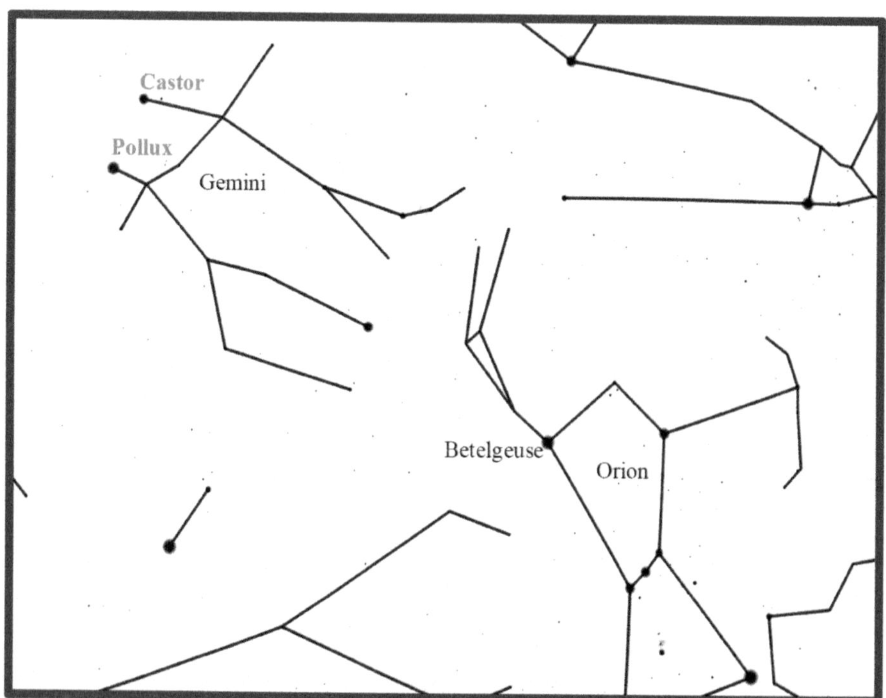

Difficulty: ☼

5. Betelgeuse (Orange-Red Star)

Yes, Betelgeuse, somewhere in the vicinity of which *The Hitchhiker's Guide to the Galaxy* is said to have been written! Kids love this star, mainly because it sounds like Beetlejuice (a film inspired by the star's name).

This big red star surprises those who think all stars are white (including me, until a few years ago). Betelgeuse also varies in brightness, over time. It is often the 8th brightest star in the sky, but it can be as bright as the 6th, or as dim as the 20th!

Betelgeuse can be found near the top of the Orion constellation. When looking at it through a telescope, it's easy to see how red it is. To contrast its redness, pan the telescope down to Rigel, a blue star detailed next.

Objects in the Orion constellation are best viewed in the winter. Most people find Orion by locating the three bright stars that make up Orion's belt.

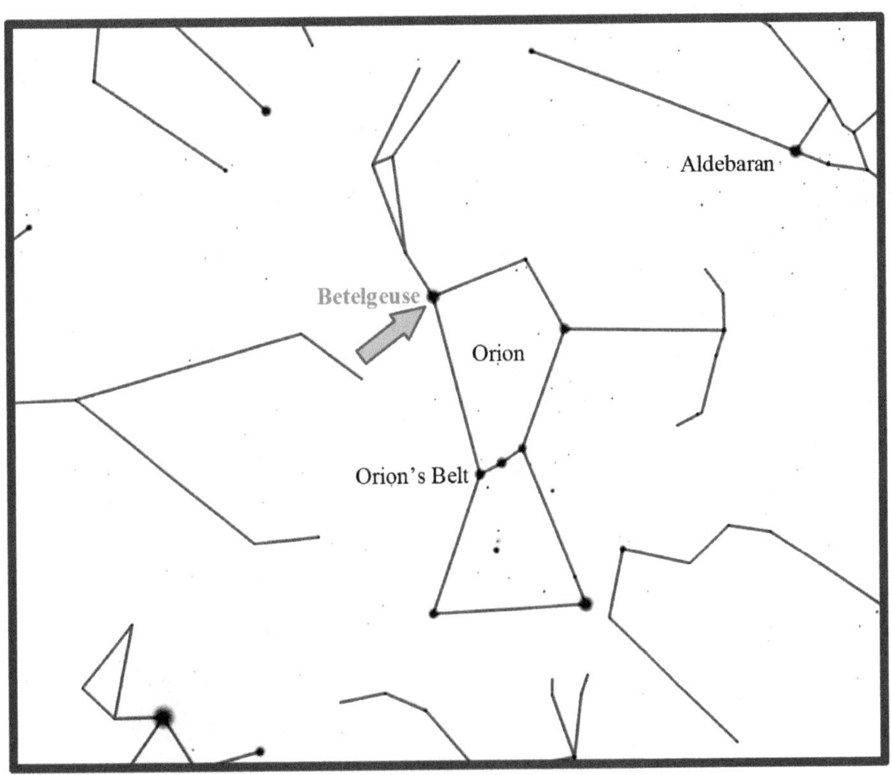

Difficulty: ☼

6. Rigel (Blue-White Star)

Not one, not two, but three stars make up this point of light found on Orion's foot. If you have very dark skies it's possible to separate star A (a Blue Supergiant) and star B (a much dimmer companion star). However, star C orbits very close to star B, and is impossible to separate using a small telescope.

If Rigel is really three stars, it must have several planets, right? The writers of Star Trek seem to think so. Fictional planets named Rigel X, Rigel II, and Rigel VII make the Rigel system about the most popular place in the Star Trek Universe!

As of March 2016, no planets have been discovered around Rigel. However, thousands of new planets are being found each year. You can find an updated database of these discoveries at http://exoplanets.org/.

While observing, remember to contrast Rigel's color and brightness against Betelgeuse.

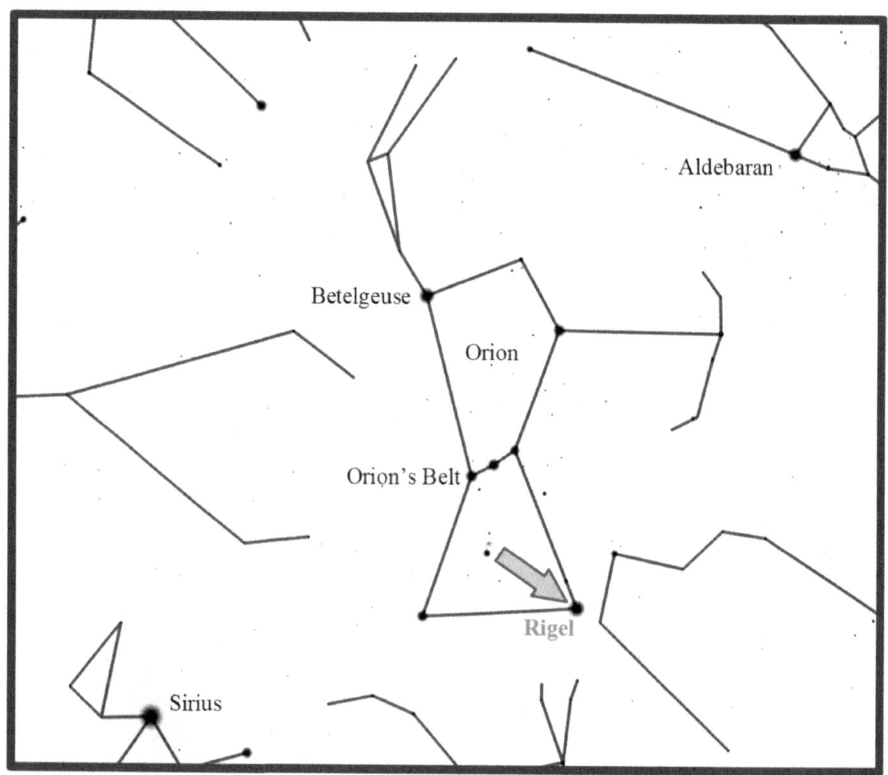

7. Sirius in Canis Major

Sirius is the first stop of the Harry Potter tour (many star names and constellations are mentioned in the Harry Potter series). This star is twice as bright as any other star in the sky, and will effectively ruin your night vision for up to thirty minutes! It is so incredibly bright that at high altitudes it can be seen during the day.

This star is nicknamed the "Dog Star", due to its prominence in the constellation Canis Major (Greater Dog), and inspired the phrase, "Dog days of summer". In Harry Potter, the character Sirius Black transforms into a dog. Coincidence? I don't think so. Through the telescope, Sirius appears as a shining diamond; when this star is low in the sky (as it often is) you may notice a shimmering array of colors. When a star or planet is near the horizon, its light travels through a greater amount of atmosphere than when the star is overhead. Disturbances in the air cause the shimmering; it's kind of like looking at a light from the bottom of a swimming pool.

Sirius is located to the left of the Orion constellation, and can be seen prominently in the southern sky during the fall, winter, and early spring.

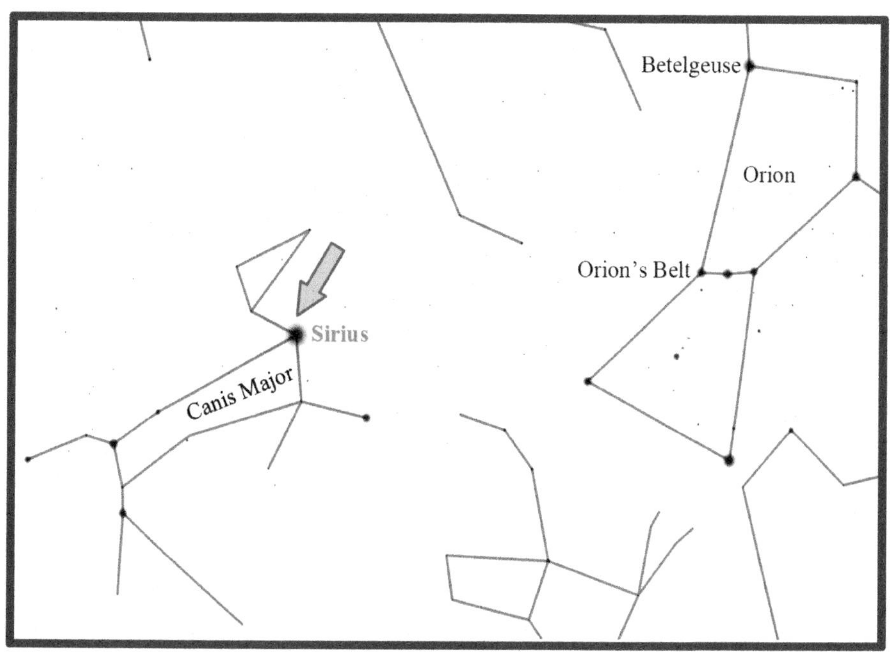

Difficulty: ☼

8. Draco

This is another stop along the Harry Potter astronomical tour. But since all of the stars in the constellation Draco are pretty dim, they are not the reason that this item is on this list.

If you know any Latin, then you may know that Draco means dragon. If you look at the constellation, you will see the dragon's head; and every October, this dragon breathes fire! The October Draconids are meteors that appear to shoot from the head of the dragon. One of my favorite activities is to lay on my back and trace the stars in this long constellation from head to tail. When I do, I almost always see a shooting star.

For a cool photo, put your camera on a tripod, point it at Draco, and take 30 second exposures for an hour or so. If you don't have a camera with manual exposure, use the fireworks setting. You might just get a newsworthy photo of this real fire-breathing dragon.

The brightest star is called Eltanin (Gamma Draconis), but if you are up for a challenge, the star Tyl (Epsilon Draconis) is a binary star visible in telescopes with at least four inches of aperture.

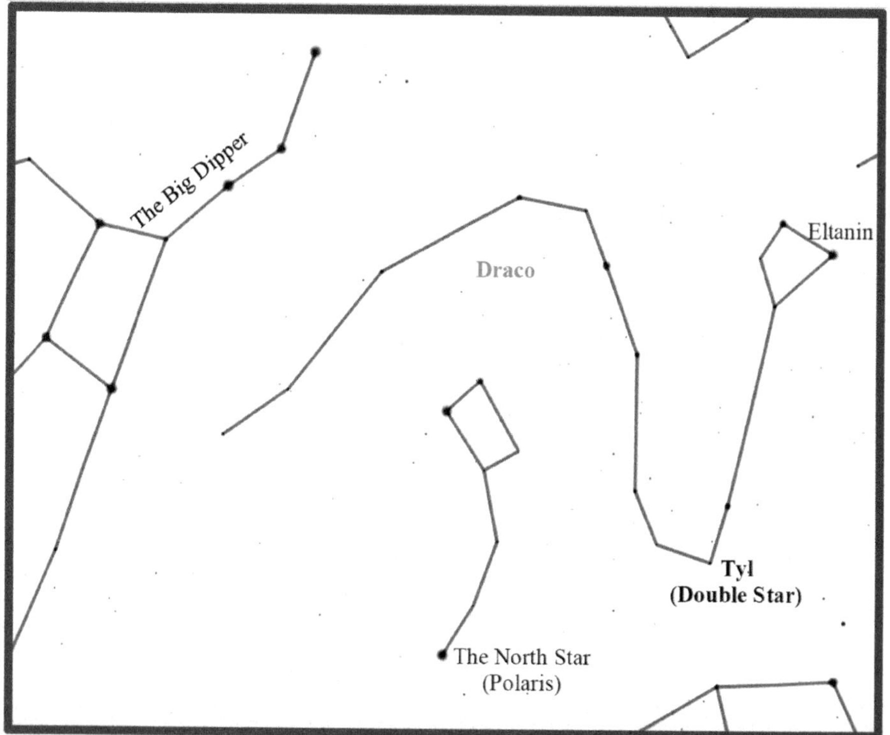

Difficulty: ☼☼

9. Vega in Lyra

Yes, Jodie Foster's home planet; just kidding (the extraterrestrial radio array, from the book and movie *Contact*, is located at Vega).

Interestingly, Vega was the North Star about twelve thousand years ago, and it will be again about twelve thousand years from now. This is due to the Earth's precession around its axis.

Precession is a property of rotating objects. You can observe precession directly in spinning toys such as a gyroscope or top. A gyroscope will precess if you tap it, by way of a smooth wobble. For the Earth, precession is mainly the result of the gravitational influence of the Sun and the Moon.

Vega is the brightest star in the constellation Lyra, and is visible high in the sky during the summer. I identify Vega by either the diamond in the constellation Lyra, or its position in the Summer Triangle. Within Lyra is the famous Ring Nebula, a target we'll explore later.

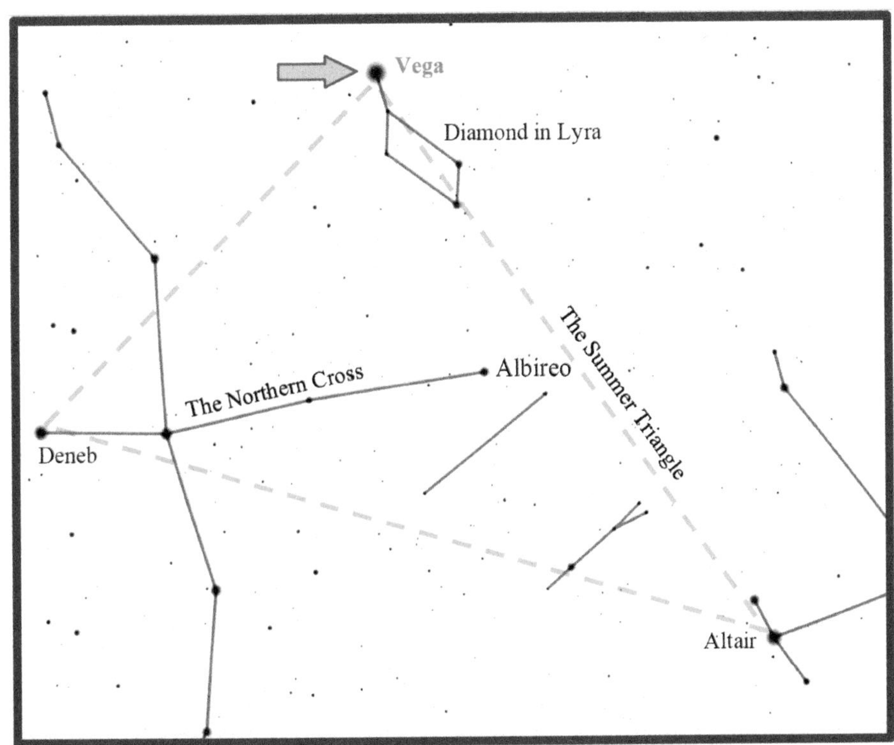

Difficulty: ☼

10. Regulus in Leo

Springtime for astronomers is sometimes referred to as "galaxy season". This is because galaxy rich constellations like Virgo and Leo are high in the sky. Leo (the Lion) boasts two popular groups of galaxies that lie just outside the range of the small telescope, in all but the darkest skies. They're called the Leo Triplet and the M96 Group. These, along with the double star Algieba, are covered in detail in the sequel to this book, *50 Targets for the Mid-Sized Telescope.*

Regulus (Alpha Leonis), the heart of the lion, is the brightest star in Leo, and is located at a relatively close 79 light-years. Later in this book, we'll discuss occultation, when a star hides behind the Moon. For Regulus, occultation is a relatively frequent event, as the moon passes quite close to this star about once a month.

Through a telescope, Regulus is a double star, though it's so bright compared to its companion, you might want to use a Moon filter (these often come with your telescope) to cut down on the glare.

Leo is most easily identified by the "Sickle". This asterism is identified by a reverse question mark that represents the Lion's mane.

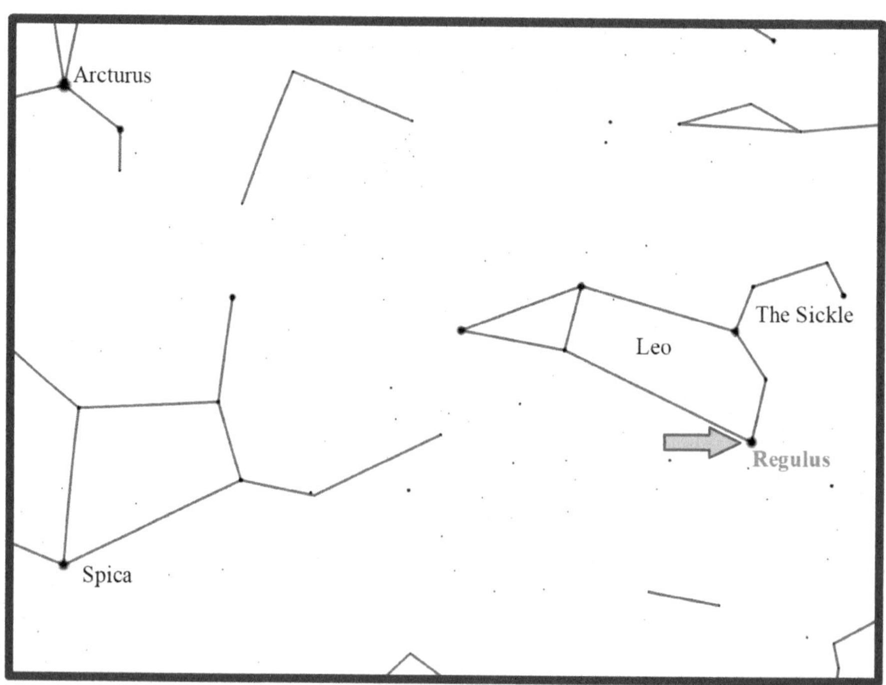

Difficulty: ☼

11. Cassiopeia (The Big W)

Cassiopeia (which I like to call the Big W) is best viewed beginning in autumn evenings, and can be used as a guide post pointing to many of the night sky's most interesting targets. For example, later in this book we'll use Cassiopeia to find the Andromeda Galaxy and the Double Cluster. In the sequel, *50 Targets for the Mid-Sized Telescope*, we'll use Cassiopeia to find targets like the E.T. Cluster and Kemble's Cascade (these are also great small telescope and binocular targets).

Cassiopeia is located near the north celestial pole (where the North Star is). For this reason, as the earth rotates, the Big W appears to moves up and over the North Star (it follows a similar motion throughout the year). So, depending on the time of night (and time of year), the constellation may appear to face one way or the other.

Cassiopeia's brightest star is called Shedir, and often appears in photos beside the Pacman Nebula, a target suitable for astrophotography, but outside the grasp of amateur telescopes in all but the darkest skies.

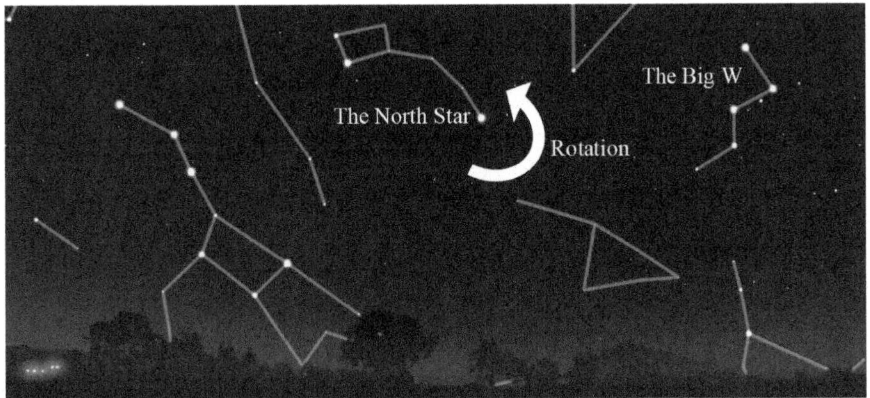

The Big W on an autumn evening (top image), and several hours (or a few months) later (bottom)

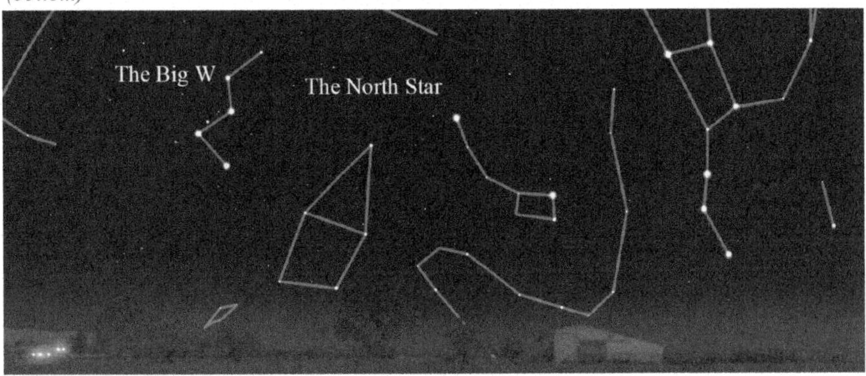

Difficulty: ☼

12. The Teapot and the Rake

In the summer, I can't think of any two constellations that contain more interesting things to see than Sagittarius and Scorpius. Why? Because between these constellations lies the direction of the exact center of our Galaxy. This part of the sky is filled with star clusters and nebulae of all shapes and sizes. This is also the direction of our Galaxy's central supermassive black hole. However, to view the region of space near the black hole, you need a telescope that can see through interstellar dust. Fortunately, scientists (like my astrophysics professor) have access to radio telescopes and space based x-rays that do just that!

The stars in the central part of Sagittarius form an asterism that looks like a teapot, while the upper most stars in Scorpius form a pattern that looks like a rake. Throughout this book (and *50 Targets for the Mid-Sized Telescope*), we'll use those descriptions as we explore the stars and other objects in this part of the sky.

If navigating this part of the sky for the first time, start with Antares, a star so red it is often confused with Mars. Pan your telescope along the imaginary lines that make up the Rake to discover several tight groupings of stars. On your way over to the teapot, explore the area in between; you'll be sure to encounter several star clusters along the way.

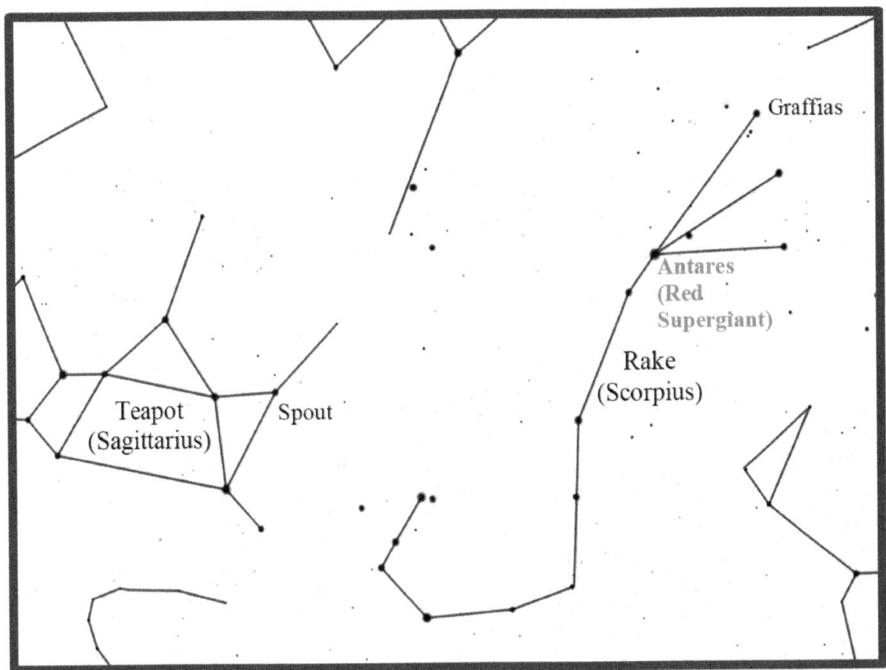

Difficulty: ☼

Part Two

Planets and Moons

The Moon is probably the most observed object in the sky (partly because it's possible to observe the Moon in the daytime, too). Each night, the Moon will be in a slightly different position, and a slightly different phase (new, crescent, quarter, gibbous, or full). Because sunlight hits the Moon differently during each phase, different features appear every night (and the cycle repeats every 29.5 days).

Planets change, too, although the changes may take weeks, months, or years to observe. They may appear smaller or larger depending on where they are, relative to the Earth. Venus has phases just like our moon, while Saturn's rings change orientation. Jupiter's moons change position each night, while Neptune's moon Triton orbits every six days. As you can see, there's always an excuse to set up your telescope!

If you have a phone adapter, the Moon and planets are great objects to photograph! I'm not saying this is easy, as it does require practice. Start with video, and don't touch your setup when the camera is recording. This will cause the image to blur. If your telescope came with a "Moon filter", attach this to your eyepiece before attaching the phone. The filter will increase the clarity of your image.

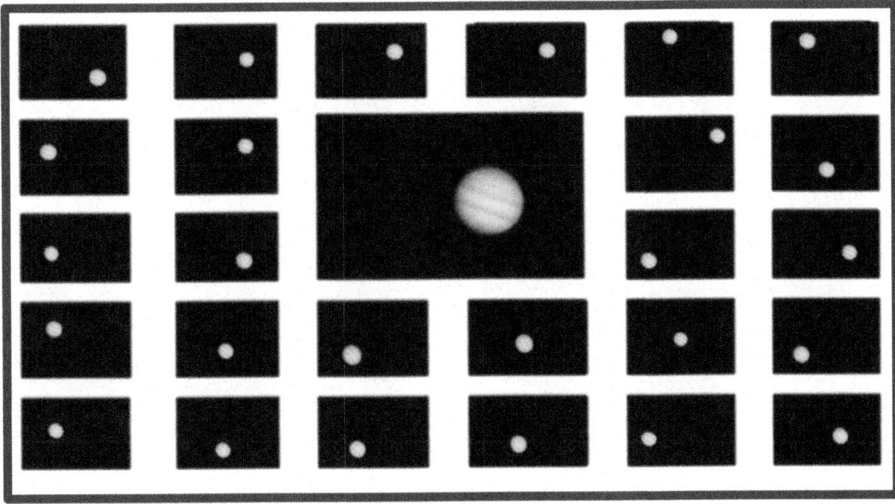

Photographs of Jupiter by children aged 3-12 at the Lafayette Library Astroblast

13. The Moon

You can't miss it! With even the smallest scopes, you should be able to clearly see the craters on the surface.

I once used that telescope I purchased at the pharmacy for $13.99 to try to film NASA's "Lcross" mission. During this mission, NASA crashed a spacecraft into the Moon. Scientists were attempting to create a plume of Moon dust they could then analyze for traces of water. The crash was supposed to create a flash of light visible from Earth, but I didn't see anything. However, the crash was not visible because the spacecraft (which crashed into a southern crater) impacted into lunar soil with the consistency of snow!

The Moon is visible for about half the month in the evening sky. If you really think about it, this makes sense, because, as most of us know, the Moon orbits the Earth every 27 days (this is one sidereal month), and goes through its phases every 29.5 days. I am often surprised when, on moonless nights, some folks seem to think that we can see the Moon with the use of a telescope. Just to clarify, if you can't see the Moon without a telescope, you can't see it with one.

The Royal Astronomical Society of Canada (RASC) has an amazing program for exploring the Moon. With detailed charts, and even a certificate program, it's not hard to spend dozens of evenings concentrating on nothing but the Moon. Check it out by following the link below.[1]

Moon through a telescope (Low Magnification (iPhone Photo)

Moon through a telescope (about 100x) (iPhone Photo)

[1]https://www.rasc.ca/observing/explore-the-moon-observing-certificate

14. Mercury

Due to Mercury's extreme proximity to the Sun, this planet can be extremely challenging to get a good look at. It may only appear in the evening sky a few days per year. As with Venus, you see Mercury in phases. These phases greatly affect its brightness. When Mercury is visible, it is only visible for a very short time before sunrise and after sunset.

To find the best time to see Mercury use astronomy software such as Stellarium, and click and lock (hit spacebar) onto Mercury. Then, use the "time" setting to fast forward until Mercury is above the horizon after sunset. You can also pay attention to astronomy websites, as they'll often let you know when Mercury is visible.

When observing Mercury through your telescope, it may look extremely bright, and even shimmer as if it is on fire. Mercury's apparent brightness is due to its proximity to the Sun, but the shimmering is due to its apparent proximity to the horizon. When you view objects that are low in the sky, you are looking through more atmosphere than when the objects are overhead. The atmospheric distortion makes the object appear to shimmer.

Mercury imaged by the Messenger Spacecraft

Mercury through a telescope

Difficulty: ✡✡✡

15. Venus

Ah, Venus! This beautiful planet is named after the Roman goddess of Love and Beauty. Venus is closer to the Sun than the Earth. For this reason, you can only see Venus shortly after sunset or right before sunrise.

Venus is bright. So bright, in fact, that Venus is one of the primary sources of UFO sightings amongst pilots. This is due to an optical illusion. Large objects viewed at great distance don't appear to move along with an observer (the person who is viewing the object). This creates the illusion that the observer is being followed by the object; in this case, Venus.

As mentioned above, Venus can either be seen just before sunrise, or just after sunset. To find Venus, use the program Stellarium to determine its specific location.

Through a telescope, Venus looks a bit like our moon. It appears white and even has phases. This is because Venus is closer to the Sun, and we sometimes see Venus's nighttime side.

When someone else looks though your telescope and says, "hey, I see the Moon!" just ask them to step back and have a look at where the telescope is pointed.

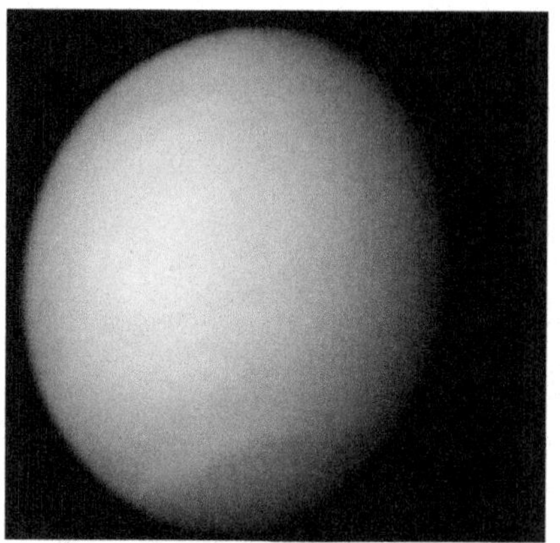

Venus imaged by the Mariner 10 Spacecraft

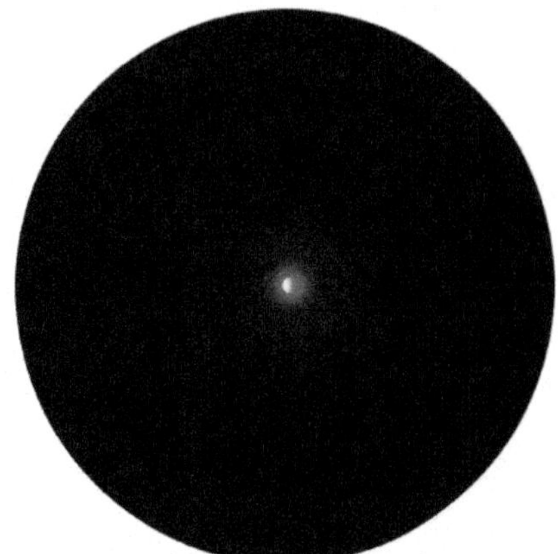

Venus through a telescope

16. Mars

Sure, it might look like just a simple red disk in your telescope, but hey, it's Mars! Keep looking and focusing, and you may be able to see the polar ice caps and some varying colors in the Martian soil.

It is very cool to realize that there are men and women here on Earth (at NASA's Jet Propulsion Laboratory in Los Angeles County) remotely piloting rovers the size of small SUVs and golf carts on the surface of Mars.

Since Mars is a planet, it will be found along the ecliptic*. As with all planets, check astronomy software like Stellarium for a precise location. If you already know Mars is visible, check the ecliptic for a deep red-looking star.

*What is the ecliptic? Since all the planets travel around the Sun in approximately the same orbital plane, they will all appear in a specific slice of the night sky; sort of like an airplane that always takes the same route. This path is called the ecliptic, and it roughly runs from the eastern horizon to the western horizon. This is also the path the Sun follows during the day.

Mars imaged by Hubble

Mars through a telescope

Difficulty: ☼☼

17. Jupiter

A view of the Solar System's largest planet, through any telescope, never ceases to impress. Be sure to admire its four largest moons: Europa, Io, Ganymede, and Callisto! For half the year, Jupiter is one of the very first things to show up in the night sky. This makes it a great target for focusing your telescope and aligning your finder scope.

Jupiter is a huge planet, being over two and a half times the mass of all the other planets in the solar system, combined. With a small telescope in good focus, not only should you be able to see the four moons discovered by Galileo in 1610, you may also see the two most pronounced cloud belts on the planet itself.

To find Jupiter, look for one of the brightest objects in the sky on the ecliptic (the path of the planets through the sky from east to west), or simply check Stellarium or other astronomy software. Use a medium powered eyepiece for optimal viewing. If you have one, a Moon filter can also bring out some of the colors.

Jupiter and its moons (moon positions change every night)

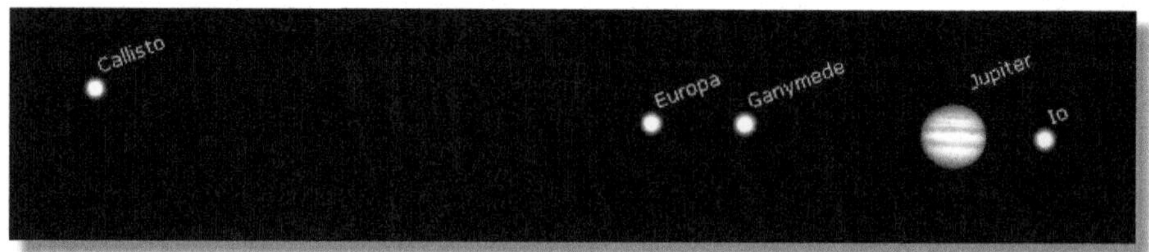

Jupiter imaged by Hubble

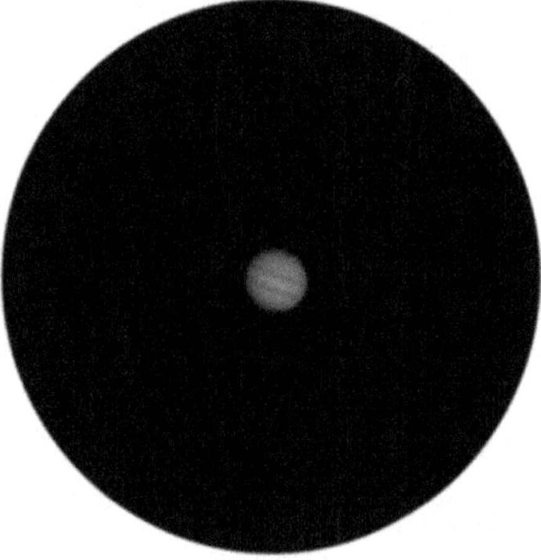

Jupiter through a small telescope (at high magnification)

Difficulty: ☼☼

18. The Moons of Jupiter

Jupiter's moons change position every night, so you'll need to use astronomy software to help you determine which moon is which.

Ganymede is the largest moon in the solar system, having over twice the mass of Earth's moon. Made famous by the 1993 television series "Power Rangers", this moon hosted the location of the Zord fleet of Mega Vehicles. How would you like to get that Jeopardy question?

Ganymede

Of Jupiter's moons discovered by Galileo, Io orbits most closely to its host planet. Io is also the most geologically active body in the solar system, sporting over four hundred active volcanoes! Due to the amount of volcanic activity, Io's surface features frequently change. Most moons in the solar system are covered with meteorite impact craters, but Io has almost none. This is because flowing lava fills them up soon after they are formed.

Io

Europa is the smallest of the four Galilean moons. Latest estimates project that beneath an icy surface, there is an ocean over 60 miles deep. By this estimate, Europa has twice as much water as there is on Earth!

Europa

Callisto has the lowest radiation levels of Jupiter's large moons, and thus, would make a promising location for human settlement! That is, if you can stand days that are 400 hours long. So, don't try to stay up all night. Callisto is usually the moon that appears farthest from Jupiter, and can be confused with a background star. In my latest science-fiction novel *Callisto Deception,* the hero, NASA engineer John Orville, travels to this moon in the year 2075.

Callisto

Difficulty: ✪✪

19. Saturn

One look at Saturn and you might trade in your car for a telescope of equal value. Or not. Either way, it's quite a sight.

Saturn's glorious rings set this planet apart from the others. In a small telescope on a clear evening, you may be able to see the gaps between the two main rings. This gap is called the Cassini Division.

The most detailed image of Saturn came from NASA's Cassini spacecraft.[1] As I'm writing this, the plutonium powered spacecraft only has a few months left before NASA will pilot it into Saturn's atmosphere, ending the probe's twenty-year mission. One of the Cassini probe's most exciting finds occurred while investigating Saturn's moon Enceladus, where it photographed over one hundred erupting geysers. The geysers spew water and molecular hydrogen from a subsurface ocean. We'll have to wait until a future mission to investigate this occurrence in more detail, but this discovery adds yet another world where scientists may search for life.

As with any planet, check your stargazing software to make sure Saturn is visible during your observing session.

Saturn through a telescope

Saturn imaged by the Cassini Spacecraft

[1] https://saturn.jpl.nasa.gov/galleries/images/

20. Titan

Titan is the largest moon of Saturn. What better place to drop out of warp to avoid detection from a Romulan mining vessel, like in the blockbuster movie *Star Trek 11.*

What is most interesting about Titan is that the gravity is low enough, and the atmosphere thick enough, that by attaching small wings to your arms, you could fly like a bird!

On January 14th, 2005, NASA landed a small probe named *Huygens* on Titan. *Huygens* penetrated Titan's thick atmosphere and parachuted to the ground. The probe took photos all the way down, and one photo from the surface (shown to the right).

Because Titan has a thick atmosphere, it also has an interesting climate. The surface temperature is almost -180 °C, and it often rains liquid methane. In addition to rain, radar images of the planet's surface confirm the existence of hydrocarbon seas and lakes.

To find Titan, first, find Saturn. Once you have found Saturn, Titan will be found orbiting beside it. On clear nights, or with a mid-sized telescope, three additional moons, Rhea, Tethys, and Dione, may also be visible.

Cassini image of Titan (near-infrared)

Saturn and Titan through a telescope

Difficulty: ✪✪✪

21. Uranus

The planet Uranus was discovered by the astronomer William Hershel, in 1781. Hershel originally believed he had discovered a comet or star, and it was two years before it officially became known as a planet.[1]

To English speakers, the most interesting thing about Uranus is its name, which shares the pronunciation with a certain private part of human anatomy. Though it sounds funny to some people, its name is very logical. Saturn is the father of Jupiter, and Uranus is the father of Saturn. It's one big family out there in the outer solar system.

Uranus and Neptune are known as the "ice giants" of our solar system. This is due to their vast distance from the Sun, and their status as gas giants (planets composed primarily of gas, that are much larger than Earth). Uranus orbits at twice the distance of Saturn, and almost twenty times the distance between the Earth and the Sun (a distance called one astronomical unit).

For the first few decades in the twenty-first century, the best time to view Uranus is in September and October. In larger telescopes, you may be able to see several of Uranus' moons.

To find Uranus, first check your astronomy software to find the precise location. Use a low magnification eyepiece, or binoculars, to make the initial find, and then move to a higher magnification eyepiece to resolve the planet and more of the its hue. Don't expect to see too see much detail; at best Uranus will appear as a hazy blue star.

Uranus imaged by the Voyager 2 Spacecraft

Uranus through a telescope

[1]NASA: Uranus: in Depth https://solarsystem.nasa.gov/planets/uranus/indepth

22. Neptune

Now that Pluto has been demoted to a “dwarf planet” by the Astronomical Union, Neptune is the farthest planet from the Sun (in our solar system). Like the other planets (besides Earth), this one is named after a Roman god, the god of the Sea.

This planet is very far from the Sun, about fifty percent farther than Uranus. It took the Voyager spacecraft twelve years to reach Neptune, and it was the last planet visited in the Voyager program’s grand tour of the Solar System.[1]

Neptune’s largest moon, Triton, is visible in telescopes like my twelve inch Dobsonian (a water-heater sized telescope currently sitting in our living room). However, this moon is most likely too dim for smaller telescopes.

Neptune, itself, is very dim, one of the dimmest objects in this book. Only telescopes six inches in diameter, or larger, will be able to resolve Neptune into a disk. For smaller telescopes, the planet will appear as a blueish point of light. However, its blue color distinguishes it from background stars. As with Uranus, use an eyepiece without much magnification to find the planet. Then, use an eyepiece with high magnification to get a better view.

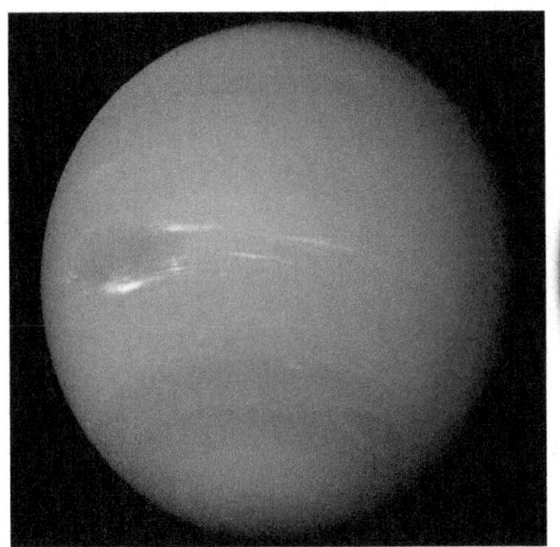

Neptune imaged by the Voyager 2 Spacecraft

Neptune through a telescope

[1]NASA: Neptune: in Depth https://solarsystem.nasa.gov/planets/naptune/indepth

Part Three

Deep-Sky Objects

Deep-sky objects are where seasoned amateur astronomers spend most of their observing time. Most folks start with the "Messier Catalogue": a list of 110 objects recorded by Charles Messier in the 1770's. Messier was a comet hunter, and his list was composed of "frustrating (to him)" objects that were **not** comets (examples include: M1, the Crab Nebula, and M42, the Orion Nebula). Little did he know that his list would be immortalized as a compilation of some of the most interesting objects in the sky.

Seasoned astronomers, with larger telescopes, often pursue targets from other lists, such as the Caldwell Catalogue: a 109-item extension to the Messier Catalogue, that basically summarizes the next best 110 targets. Examples from the list include C-14, the Double-Cluster, and C-4, the Iris Nebula (we'll explore the Iris Nebula in *50 Targets for the Mid-Sized Telescope*).

The most comprehensive list of deep-sky objects is called the New General Catalogue (NGC). This list contains 7,840 items. This list overlaps with both Messier's list and the Caldwell Catalogue.

M42 photographed with my four inch Explore Scientific Refractor

23. The Milky Way

If you're an amateur astronomer (if you own a telescope, that's you) and you can't find the Milky Way, you need to find darker skies! In fact, all of the stars that you see in the night sky are part of the Milky Way. When we say we see the Milky Way, we're are actually referring to the *plane* of the Milky Way. You can clearly see the plane in the photo, below.

If you live near a large town or city, you probably cannot see the white wispiness that makes up the plane of the Milky Way. In fact, the maximum number of visible stars in the sky from within a large city is only about a dozen. Far from city lights, you might count as many as 6000 stars on a moonless night. The Milky Way contains between 300 billion and 400 billion stars! That is why it appears as a white wispiness in truly dark skies.

One of the ways to explore the plane of the Milky Way with a telescope is to start at one horizon and work your way across to the other. With patience, you'll find many star clusters beyond what's mentioned in this book.

Milky Way from Hawaii. Author's photo.

Difficulty: ☼

24. The Orion Nebula (M42)

The Orion Nebula is often dubbed the "Star Factory". When you observe this nebula, you can see a great expanse of gas surrounding a series of stars. It is called the "Star Factory" because these stars are being formed out of that gas.

The Orion Nebula is part of the Orion Molecular Cloud Complex, which also contains the Horsehead Nebula. Although the Horsehead is far too dim to see in a small telescope, it is nonetheless the location of "The Planet of the Ood" from BBC's classic series *Doctor Who.*

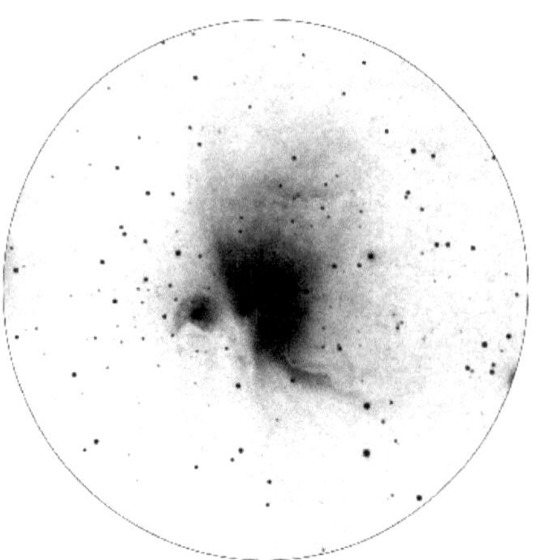

Orion Nebula through a telescope

The Orion Nebula is one of the easiest to find deep-sky objects (objects not located in our Solar System). To locate the nebula, find Orion's belt, and then imagine his sword as the line of stars running down from the belt. The middle of this sword contains the Orion Nebula.

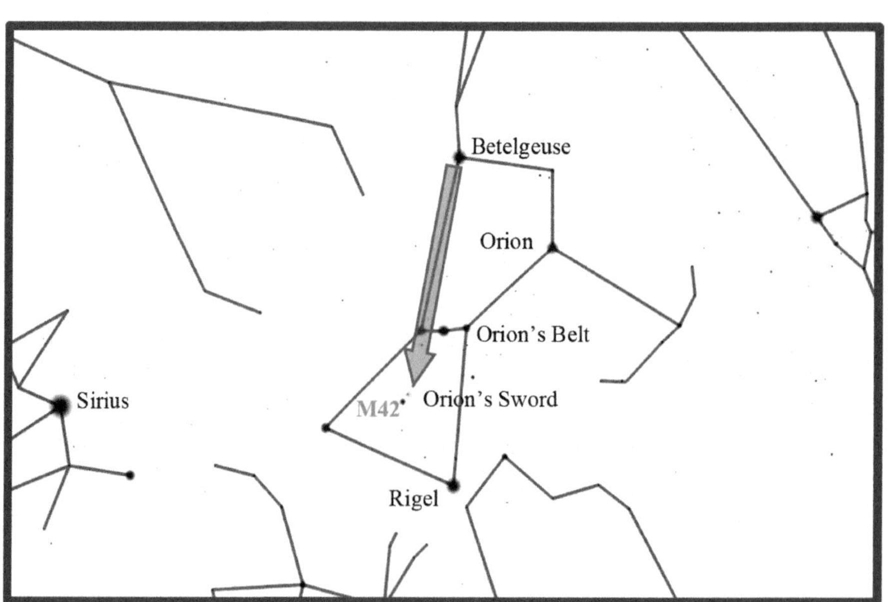

Difficulty: ✡✡

25. The Hyades

The Hyades, residing in the center of the constellation Taurus, is the nearest open star cluster, and thus makes for a great target for binoculars or small telescopes. It is best viewed during the winter months, as it precedes Orion in its path through the sky. Visually, the cluster is accented by the red giant star Aldebaran. However, this is simply a chance coincidence. Aldebaran is not actually a part of the cluster at all, as it lies much closer to Earth.

The cluster features a bright naked-eye double star, Theta Tauri, or θ Tau for short. The individual stars are designated θ^1 Tauri and θ^2 Tauri. On close inspection with a telescope, you should be able to make out a color difference between the two stars of almost equal brightness (one appears slightly orange, and the other white).

The Hyades as viewed through binoculars, or a very wide field telescope eyepiece

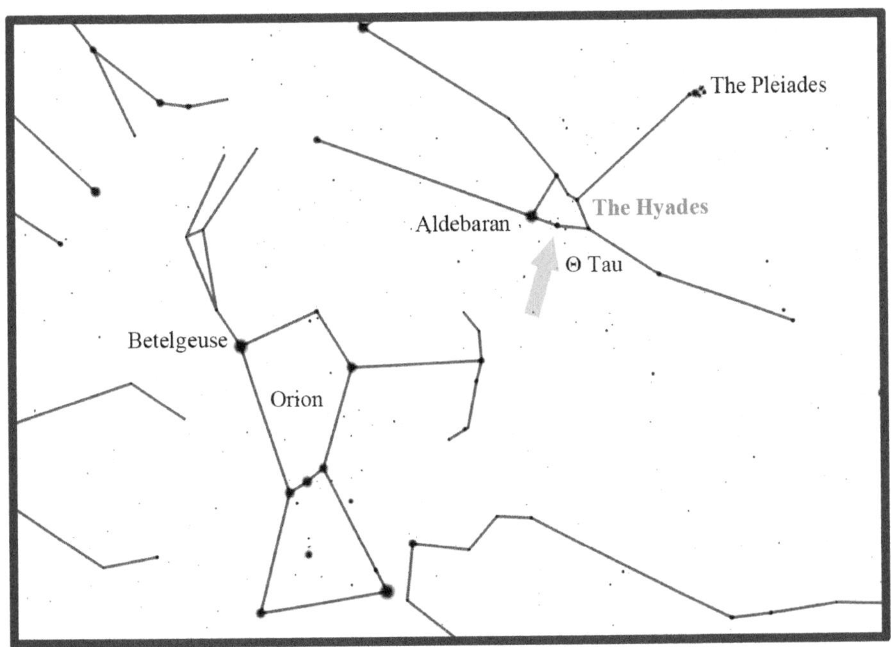

26. The Pleiades (M45)

You can skip this one if you drive a Subaru, because you see this star cluster every time you look at your steering wheel. If you don't drive a Subaru, then the Pleiades can be found to the right of Orion (that's your right, Orion's left). According to Greek mythology, the Pleiades, or Seven Sisters, were turned into stars by Zeus to help them flee Orion, who, ironically, still pursues them through the night sky.

Some people think that this cluster of stars is the Little Dipper. It's not. The actual Little Dipper is quite dim, yet considerably larger than the Pleiades, and is located in the northern sky.

To find the Pleiades, look up and to the right of Orion. Usually, with any amount of light pollution, only 6 of the brightest stars in the Pleiades are visible to the unaided eye. However, as soon as you look in your telescope, dozens of stars will appear!

The Pleiades through a telescope

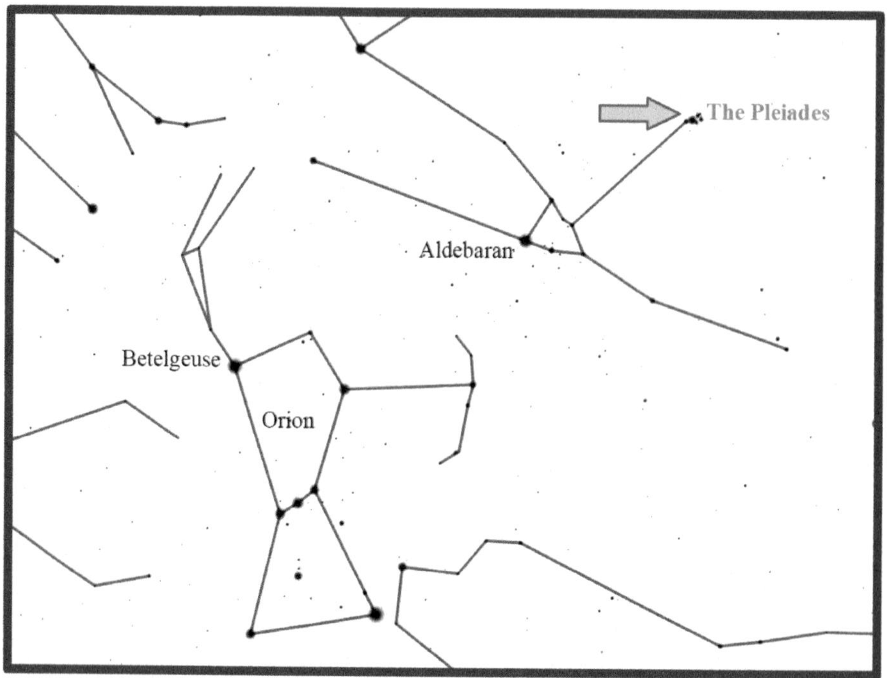

27. The Hercules Star Cluster (M13)

Deep-Sky Objects

This globular cluster is one of only a few objects in this book that resides outside the plane of the Galaxy! It is also where the Earth was hidden in Dan Simmon's classic (1989) novel *Hyperion* (sorry for the spoiler).

M13, occassionally called the "Great Globular Cluster in Hercules" is one of the brightest deep sky objects. It's also relatively easy to find, because it's one of the largest globular clusters, containing several hundred thousand stars. If you are using binoculars or a very small telescope, M13 will appear as a grey glob (hence globular).

To find M13, search the side of the Keystone (an asterism in Hercules); pan around the edge of the square until you find it.

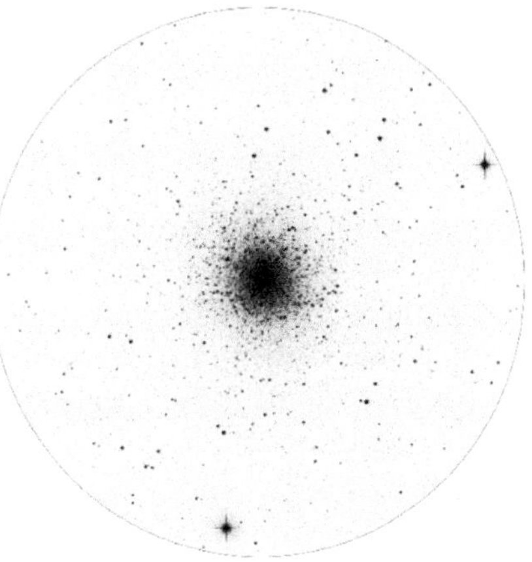

Hercules Star Cluster through a telescope

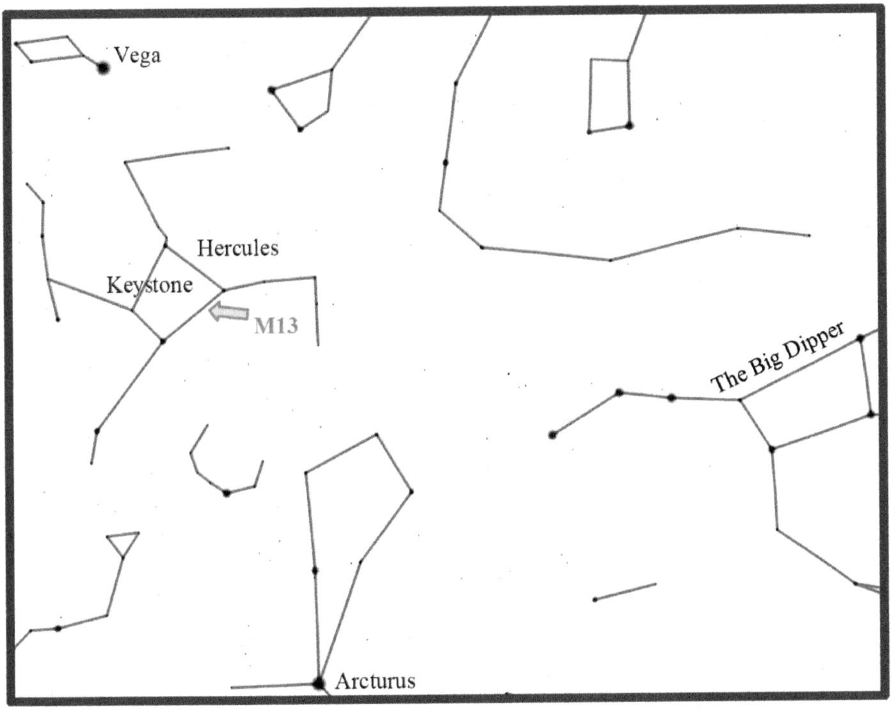

Vega
Hercules
Keystone
M13
The Big Dipper
Arcturus

Difficulty: ☼☼☼

28. The Andromeda Galaxy (M31)

Before the twentieth century, the Milky Way was thought to be the only galaxy in the universe. Astronomers dubbed objects that seemed to reside outside of the galaxy "Island Universes". It wasn't until Edwin Hubble measured the distance to the Andromeda Galaxy that debate over the Island Universes closed. Before Hubble, many astronomers believed that the Andromeda Galaxy was actually a nebula, and called it *The Andromeda Nebula*.

The cool thing about the Andromeda Galaxy is that it is over six times as wide as the full Moon! However, the only way to see the full extent of this galaxy is through long exposure photography. When you see the Andromeda Galaxy in your telescope, you only see the bright galactic core, which appears as a beautiful grey smudge.

To find the Andromeda Galaxy, use the constellation Cassiopeia. Observe the distance between any two stars in the W, then count three of these lengths in the direction (away from the North Star) shown below.

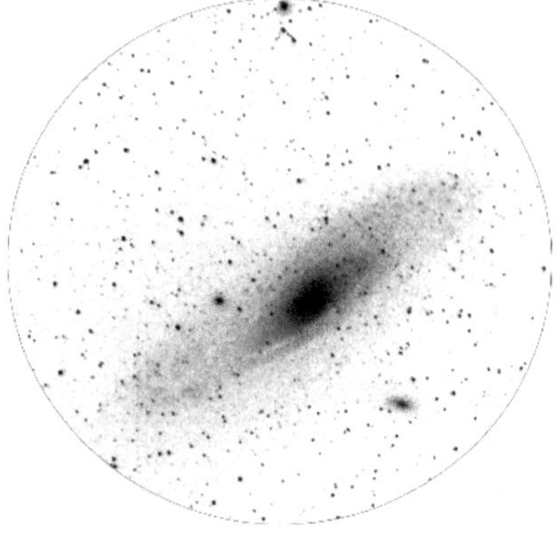

Andromeda Galaxy through a telescope

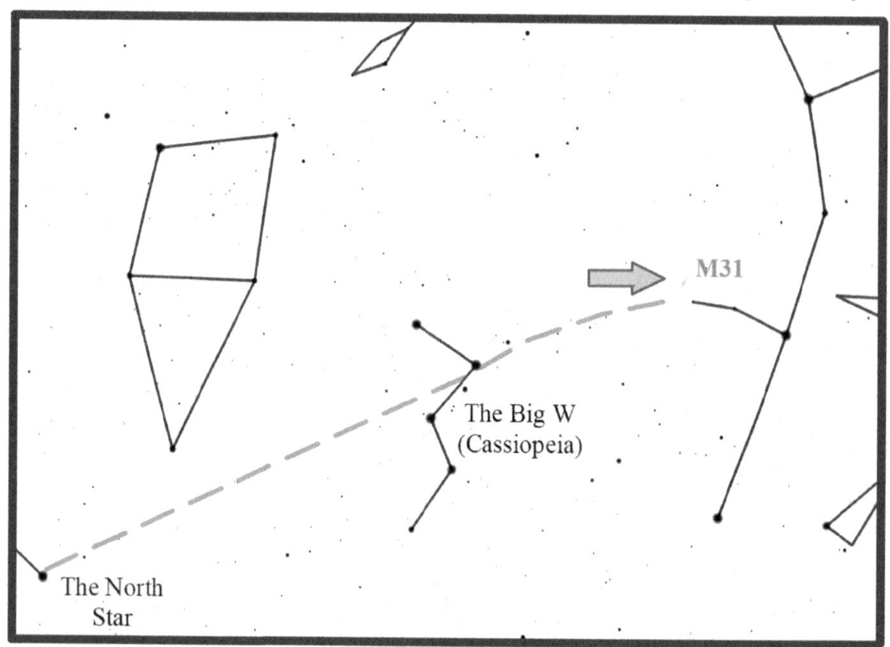

29. The Dumbbell Nebula (M27)

Deep-Sky Objects

Discovered in the year 1764 by the French astronomer Charles Messier, the Dumbbell Nebula was the first planetary nebula ever discovered. It also has a very large apparent size in a telescope. The photo below shows its apparent size, relative to the Moon.

M27 is located in the Summer Triangle, between the constellations Vulpecula and Sagitta. Interestingly, the Dumbbell Nebula wasn't given its name until 1833, when astronomer John Herschel made this record: *"A nebula shaped like a dumb-bell, with the elliptic outline completed by a feeble nebulous light."*

Moon and M27 at the same magnification

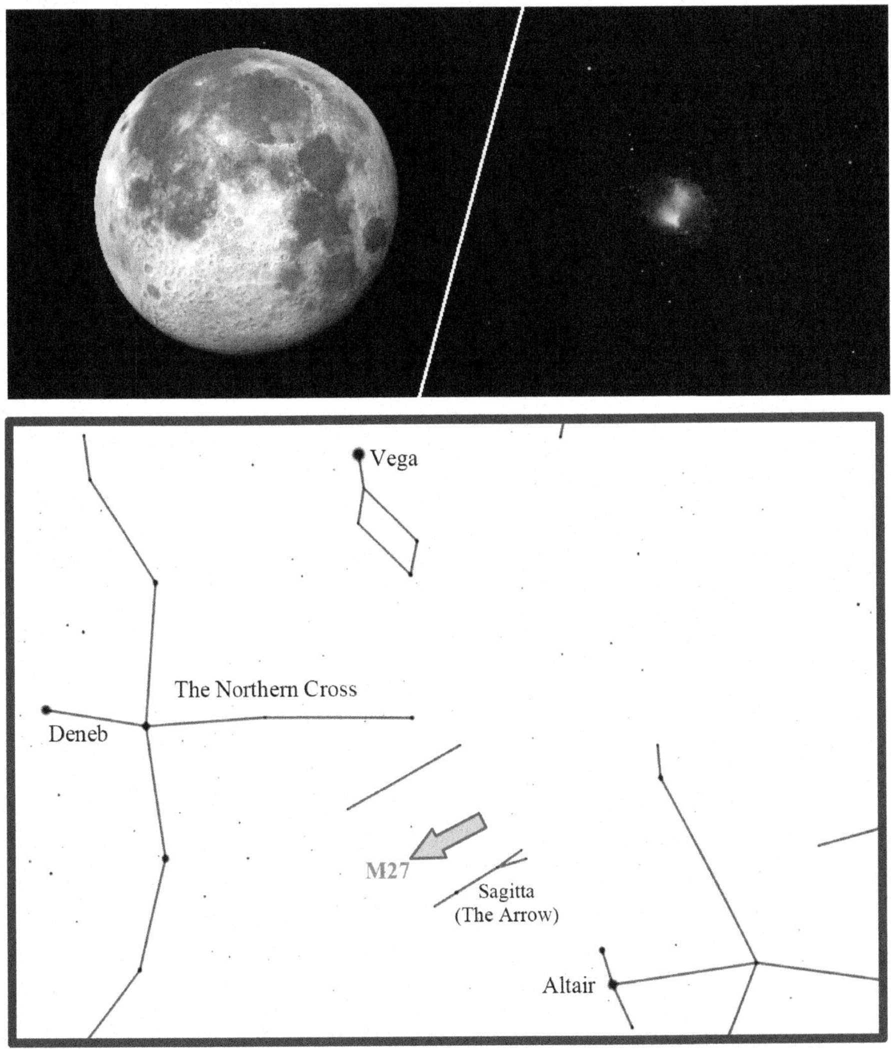

Difficulty: ☼☼☼

30. Albireo

Albireo is probably my favorite double-star to show off at stargazing events. This is due to the striking color contrast between the two stars. The brighter of the two stars, Albireo A (Beta Cygni A), appears yellow or amber, while Albireo B (Beta Cygni B) is blue. Altough this star spends most of the winter below the horizon, there is an almost identical double star, dubbed "Winter Alberio", in Canis Major. However, Winter Alberio (145 Cma) is slightly more challenging to find, so we'll save that for *50 Targets for the Mid-Sized Telescope*.

This double star is found at the base of the Northern Cross, and within the Summer Triangle. If you have a cell phone adapter for your telescope, this is a great star to photograph, as the phone's camera will accentuate the contrasting colors between the two stars.

Albireo through a telescope (in this image, the yellow star is on the left)

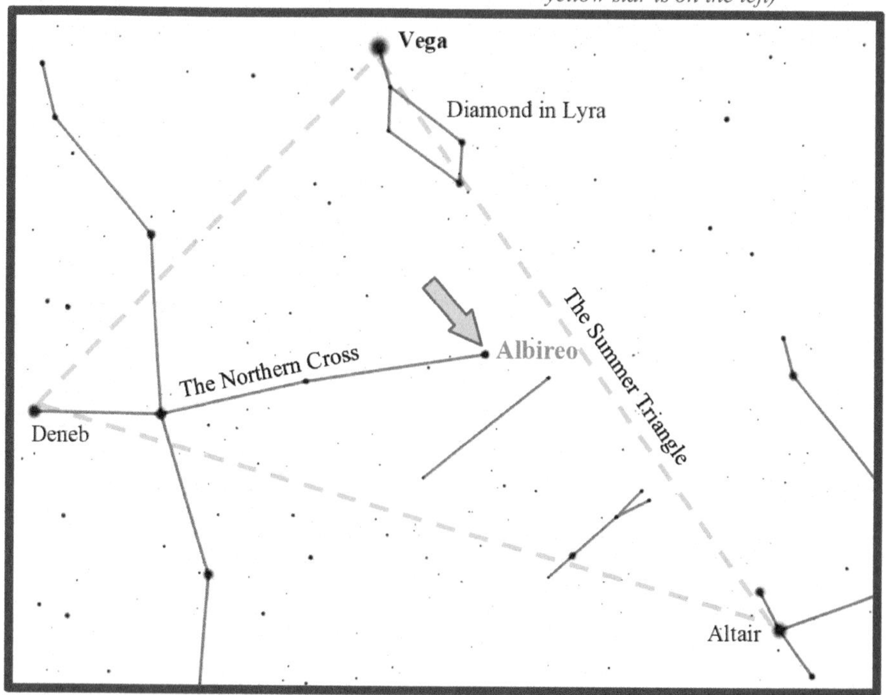

Difficulty: ☼☼

31. Mizar & Alcor

No need for optometrists when you have these two stars in sight. Nicknamed the "Horse and Rider", seeing these stars, located in the Big Dipper, used to be a test of eyesight! These days, most people can make out these two stars with corrected lenses. Mizar and Alcor make up the center of the handle of the Big Dipper.

In addition to being a visual double star, Mizar was the first telescopic double star ever observed. It was discovered by an Italian mathematician named Benedetto Castelli, in 1617.

When observing these stars, first notice the double stars which can be seen with the unaided eye, then look at the stars through the telescope. Mizar will be the star with the companion so close they appear to almost touch.

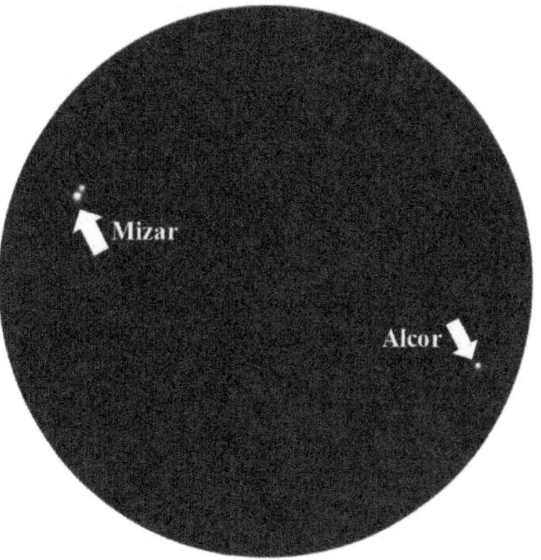

Mizar and Alcor through a telescope

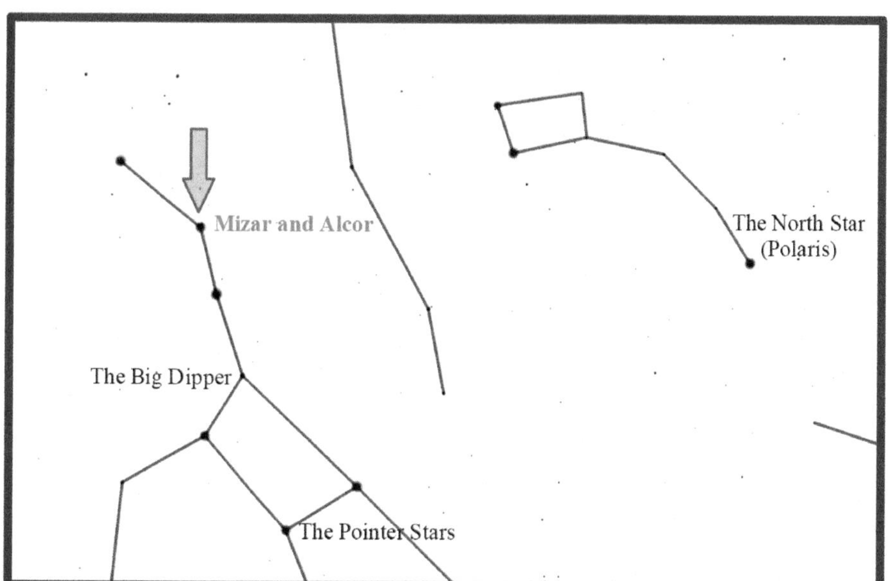

Difficulty: ☼☼

32. Double Cluster in Perseus

These star clusters are notable for two reasons. First, they are easy to find from the Northern Hemisphere, since they are above the horizon most evenings of the year. Second, each year the Perseid meteor shower originates from this part of the sky, in mid-August.

These two clusters, designated NGC 869 and NGC 884 (or Caldwell 14, together), are visible to the naked eye in extremely dark skies (a rarity in today's modern world). NGC stands for "New General Catalog", a list of almost eight thousand nebulae and star clusters compiled in the late 1800's. "Caldwell" is a catalog of 109 targets best suited for amateur astronomers.

Star clusters are great for showing just how many stars are out there! To find the double Cluster in Perseus, look to Cassiopeia (the big W) and find the clusters below and to the left of the W (or up and to the right of a big M, depending on the time and season, or time of night).

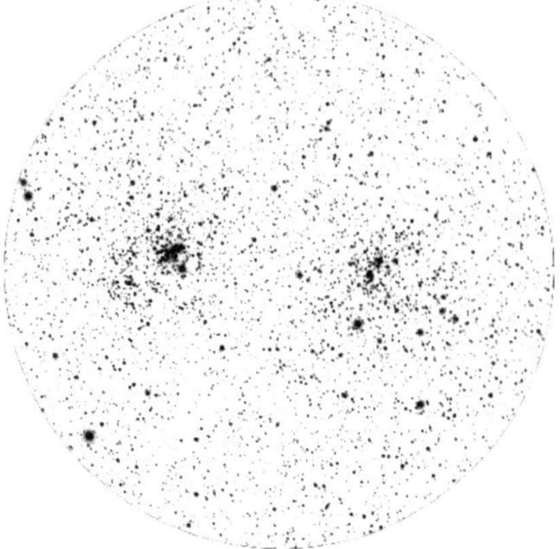

The Double Cluster at very low magnification

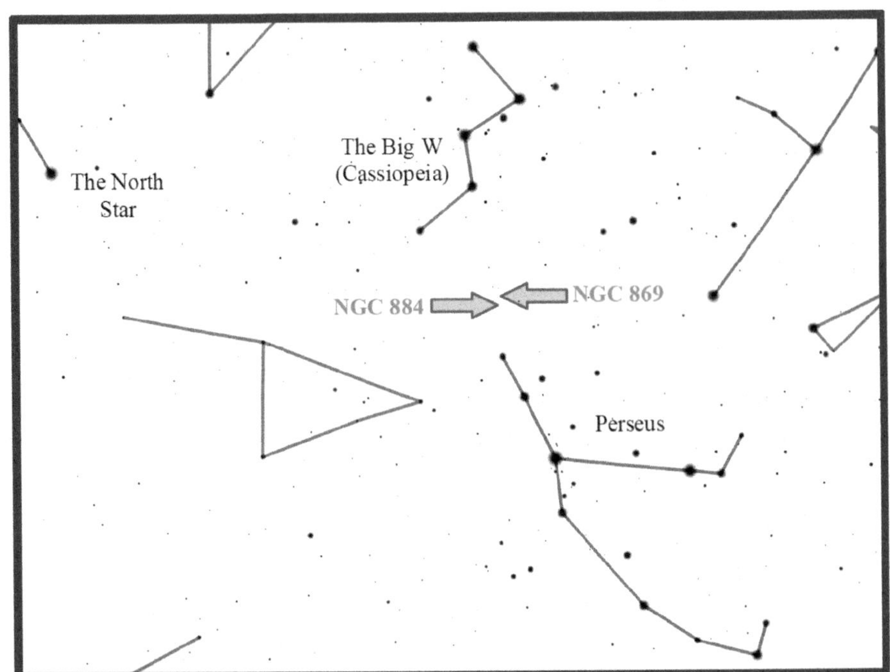

Difficulty: ✩✩✩

33. The Ring Nebula (M57)

The Ring Nebula appears about as large as Jupiter in your telescope, but not nearly as bright. The challenge, in a small telescope, is to clearly make out the hole in the Ring. In order to view the center of the Ring, you may need a telescope with a lens or mirror of at least 10cm in diameter, but the disk shape is visible in smaller telescopes. Make sure your eyes are adapted to the dark for optimal viewing, and practice "averted vision" (observing something without looking directly at it) to take advantage of the more sensitive light-detecting cells in your eye's retina.

This Nebula was formed when a red giant star shed its outer shell of ionized gas, leaving only a white dwarf star where the red giant once was.

To find the Ring Nebula, pan the telescope between the two stars opposite Vega in the Diamond pattern in the constellation Lyra.

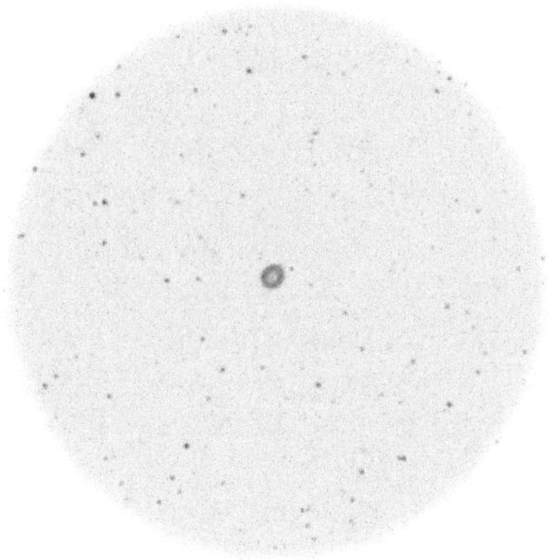

Ring Nebula through a telescope

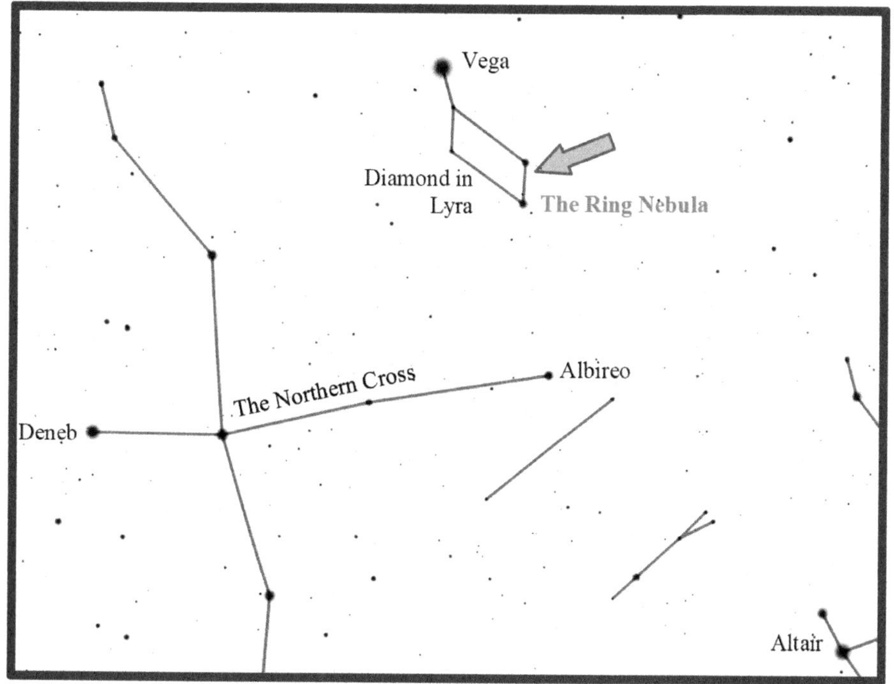

Difficulty: ☼☼☼

34. The Whirlpool Galaxy (M51)

Deep-Sky Objects

The Whirlpool Galaxy, or M51, is easy to find in a small telescope, or even binoculars, but only on moonless nights and far from city lights. This Galaxy is accompanied by a smaller companion galaxy designated NCG 5191, or M51b. The gravitational interaction between these two structures is thought to give the Whirlpool its well defined spiral shape.

Astronomers have discovered that most large galaxies have a supermassive black hole at their center, and observations of M51 by the Hubble telescope reveal a distinct X shaped pattern around this galaxy's center. One bar of the X is most likely dust circling the black hole. The second bar of the X could be dust interacting with a cone of ionized particles. Further observation is required before astronomers reach a scientific consensus.

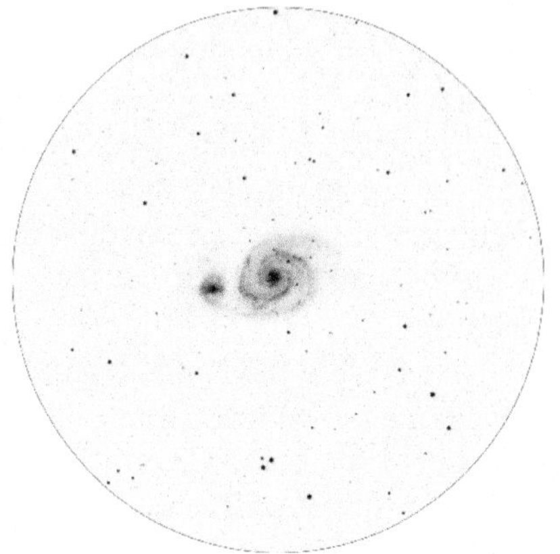

Whirlpool Galaxy through a telescope

Supernovae have also been observed in this galaxy in 1994, 2005, and 2011.

To find the Whirlpool Galaxy, make a right triangle under the handle of the Big Dipper, as shown below.

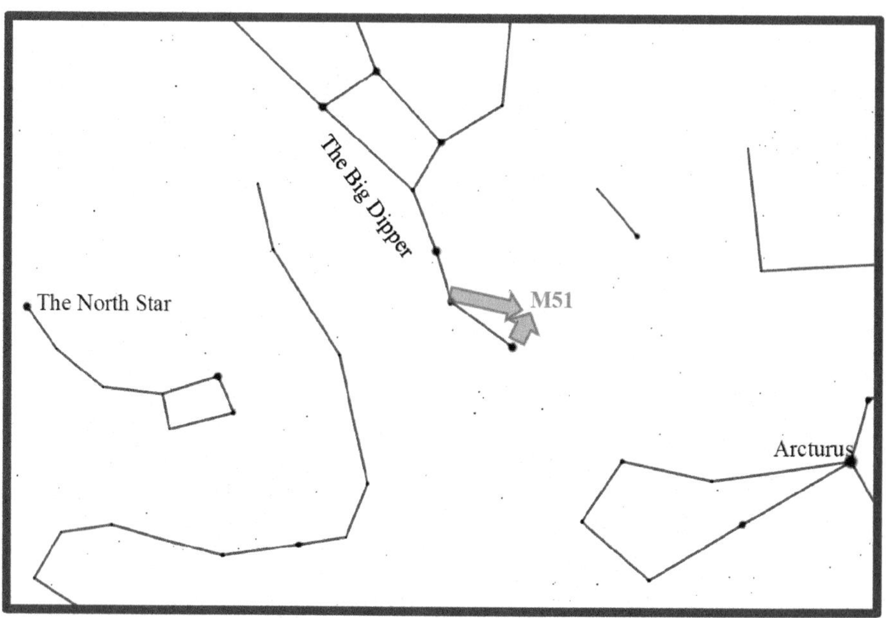

Difficulty: ☼☼☼

35. The Trifid Nebula (M20)

In the first section of this book, we introduced the Teapot in Sagittarius as a great place to explore deep-sky objects (deep-sky means objects outside of our Solar System). Even without using a star map, you're bound to run into several interesting targets. The Teapot is regarded as one of the best places to scan the sky, using binoculars.

For me, the Trifid Nebula is the easiest to identify. It can be found by lining up two of the stars in the lid of the Teapot, as shown in the map below. If you look carefully, the smudge (remember, most nebula look like beautiful smudges in a small telescope) is subdivided into three separate lobes. In addition to this complexity, within the nebulosity you may be able to resolve several small clusters of recently formed stars.

After you've admired the Trifid Nebula, search the region just below it. You should be able to find the neighboring Lagoon Nebula (M8).

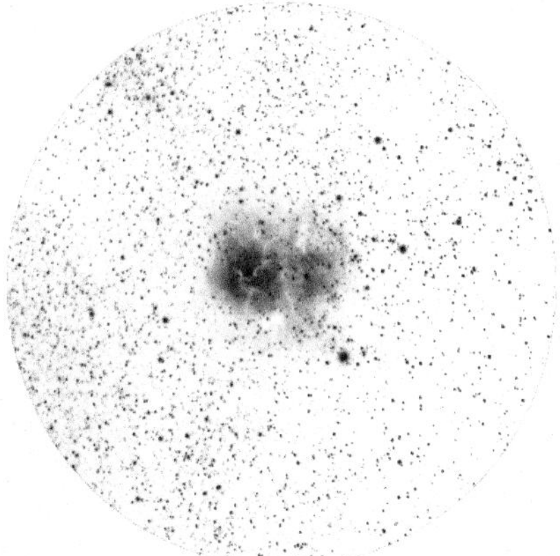

Trifid Nebula through a telescope

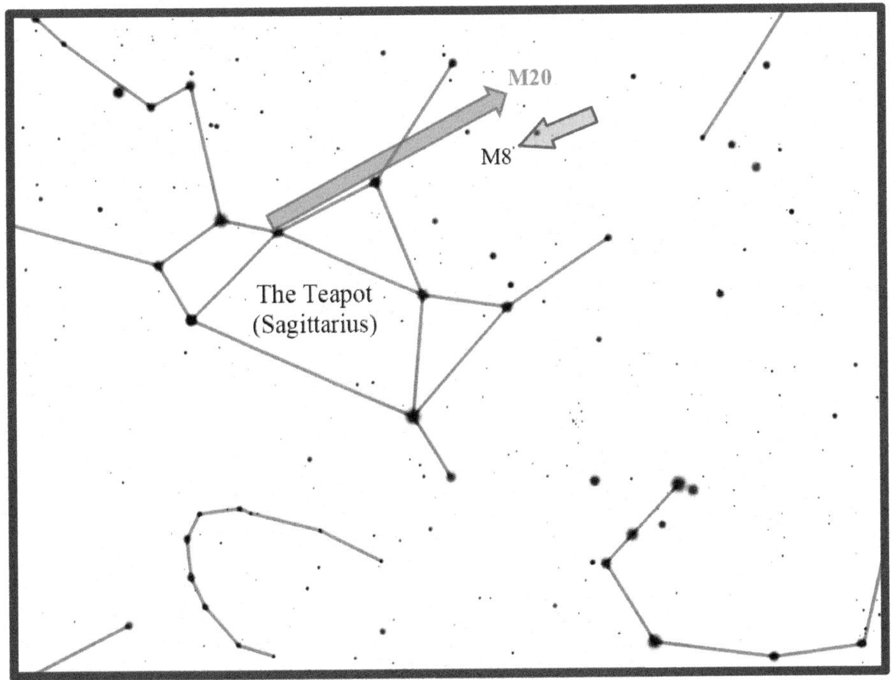

Difficulty: ✪✪✪

36. Bode's & the Cigar (M81 & M82)

After Andromeda, M81 and M82 are the two galaxies that are the easiest to find. M82 is commonly referred to as the "Cigar Galaxy", because of how it appears from Earth (M82 is a spiral galaxy viewed edge on). M81 is referred to as "Bode's Galaxy". This Galaxy was named for its discoverer, a German astronomer named Johann Elert Bode. Bode can also be blamed for suggesting the name for the planet Uranus, beating out less popular names like "Cybele", "Herschel's Planet", or "Georgium Sidus"[1].

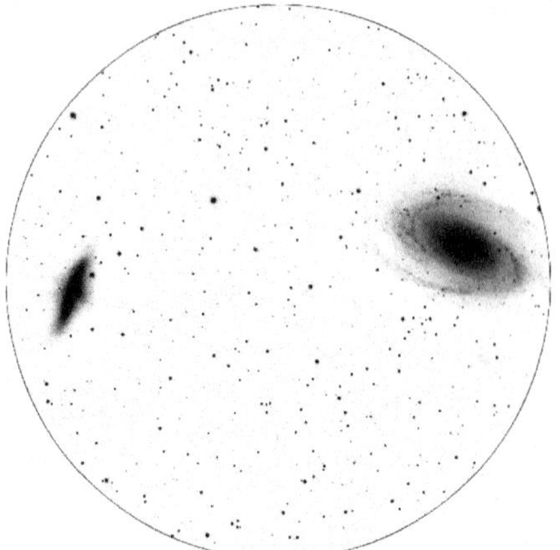

M81 and M82 through a telescope

M81 is particularly interesting to professional astronomers, because in its center is a gigantic black hole with a mass 70 million times that of our Sun!

To view these galaxies, use an eyepiece with low magnification. With the Big Dipper as a guide, create a line between the bottom left of the Dipper's cup and its lip. Then, extend this line from the lip to arrive at the location of these galaxies.

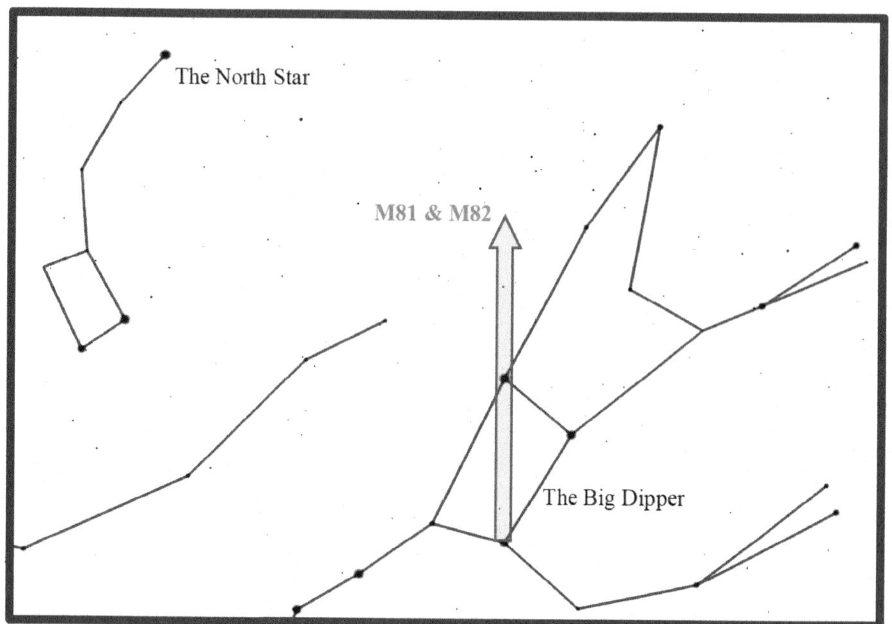

[1] Bode's Biography: http://messier.seds.org/xtra/Bios/bode.html

Difficulty: ☼☼☼

37. The Crab Nebula (M1)

Something special happened on the Fourth of July, 1054, and it wasn't American Independence Day, yet. On this day, Chinese astronomers recorded what they thought was a new star, a star brighter than Venus! After a few weeks, however, the new star dimmed, but it was still visible for almost two years, at which point the star was nearly lost to history. But in 1731, almost seven hundred years later, a British astronomer, named John Bevis, observed a blob in that exact spot. Then, almost three decades after that, the French comet hunter, Charles Messier, added this "blob" to his catalog of objects that were "definitely not comets". Messier designated the object "M1".

The Crab Nebula is a supernova remnant. The Chinese observed the actual supernova, the violent explosion of a star. Now, when you look through your telescope, you are observing an ongoing explosion of gas and dust shooting through space at almost five million kilometers per hour.

To find the Crab Nebula, use Betelgeuse and Aldebaran to identify the star Zeta Tauri. M1 will be found nearby.

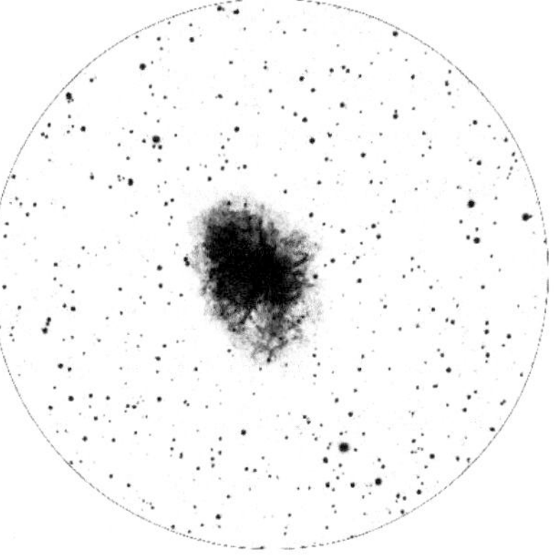

Crab Nebula through a telescope

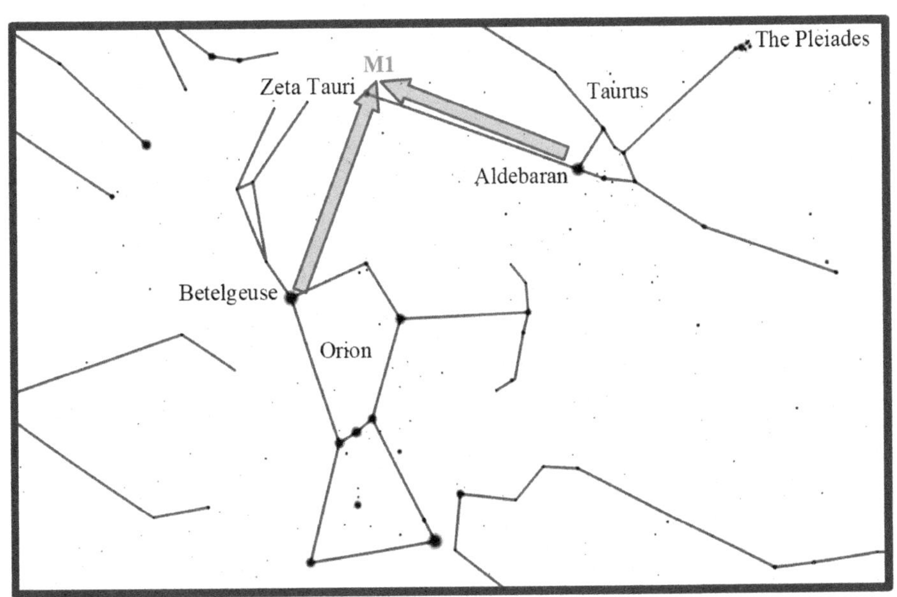

Part Four

Solar System Objects and Events

Some of the best things about joining an astronomy club are the activities centered around solar eclipses, lunar eclipses, and comets. These occurrences usually make the news, and draw large crowds to schools and parks, where members gather to share the views through their telescopes.

Viewing the Sun can be a lot of fun with a commercial solar filter (so you don't go blind), or a designated solar telescope like a Coronado. A Coronado solar telescope filters the light so you only get light from a very specific wavelength. This enables you to see features like prominences and flairs. Solar filters for your telescope allow all wavelengths (white light), and are great for viewing sunspots. Both types of telescopes are great for viewing a solar eclipse.

Coronado PST - Solar Telescope

Members of the Mount Diablo Astronomical Society witness a solar eclipse with the public

38. Lunar Eclipse

Often referred to as a Blood Moon, lunar eclipses are not as rare as you might think. Unlike solar eclipses which are only visible in certain places, lunar eclipses can be observed from almost anywhere on the nighttime side of Earth, assuming there are no clouds blocking the view of the Moon.

A lunar eclipse occurs when the Moon passes into the shadow of the Earth. Sunlight passes through the Earth's atmosphere, giving the Moon a reddish hue.

There are three basic types of lunar eclipses. First, and most exciting, is the total lunar eclipse, where the Moon is totally immersed in the Earth's shadow. Second, there is the partial lunar eclipse. During a partial eclipse, the Moon is only partially covered. Finally, there is the penumbral lunar eclipse, where light passing through the Earth's atmosphere illuminates a section of the Moon, but no distinct shadow is visible. However, penumbral eclipses are often difficult to distinguish from a regular full Moon.

A schedule of total and partial lunar eclipses, through the year 2030, has been included in the appendix.

Total lunar eclipse. Author's Photo

Partial lunar eclipse. Author's Photo

Difficulty: ☼

39. Sunspots

Sunspots are eddies, or storms, of magnetic activity near the surface of the Sun. These storms reduce the surface temperature over a given area, and create the dark spots visible in solar filtered telescopes.

What's cool about sunspots? Well, first, they are usually about the size of the Earth! Second, they come in pairs (one for each magnetic pole of the disturbance). Third, they change location every day (mainly due to the rotation of the Sun). Fourth, I once took a photo of a sunspot that looked like Hawaii.

To view sunspots, use a commercial solar filter over your telescope or binoculars, and then get the Sun in good focus. With the Sun in focus, you should almost always be able to see at least one or two sunspots.

Remember, never look at the Sun without a commercial solar filter on the primary mirror or lens (not the eyepiece) of your telescope.

Photographing the Sun using solar filtered binoculars and an iPhone

Difficulty: ☼☼☼

40. Solar Eclipse

A solar eclipse occurs when the Moon passes in front of the Sun. Due to the elliptical orbit of the Moon, sometimes the eclipse happens when it's closer to the Earth, and sometimes it happens when it's farther away. For this reason, there are two types of eclipses. First, there is the annular eclipse, where the Moon is farther away and cannot completely cover the Sun. Second, there is the total solar eclipse, when the Moon orbits close to the Earth and fully blocks out the Sun.

I admit that I will not witness a total solar eclipse until the next one in summer 2017, but I hear that viewing a total solar eclipse is an amazing experience; the air gets cooler, animals do strange things, and it gets considerably darker.

I have only experienced an annular eclipse, which is how I was able to take the photo below (using my iPhone, binoculars, and a solar filter).

For the hour both before and after totality, you can view the Sun through your telescope using a commercial solar filter. Totality is when the Moon fully covers the Sun. This can last anywhere from thirty seconds to six minutes.

A schedule for all solar eclipses, through the year 2030, is included in the appendix of this book.

Annular Solar Eclipse - May 20th, 2012

Difficulty: ☼☼☼

41. Ceres & Vesta

You may know about the asteroid belt between Mars and Jupiter, but most folks don't realize its sparseness. Even in the asteroid belt, space is very, very empty. The asteroid Ceres makes up a third of all the mass in the entire belt. The mass of all the asteroids combined is less than 4% of the mass of our Moon!

In 2006, the International Astronomical Union reclassified Ceres as a dwarf planet (like Pluto). Vesta, due to its smaller mass, is classified as a minor planet.

To see Ceres or Vesta, use astronomy software the same as you would for a planet. Ceres and Vesta are quite small and look like stars through a telescope, so if you're not sure which point of light is the asteroid, sketch the location of the brightest stars in that area. Observe the same location in a few days, and the asteroid is the object that moved. Ceres and Vesta can even be seen without a telescope, in extremely dark skies.

Vesta imaged by the Dawn Spacecraft

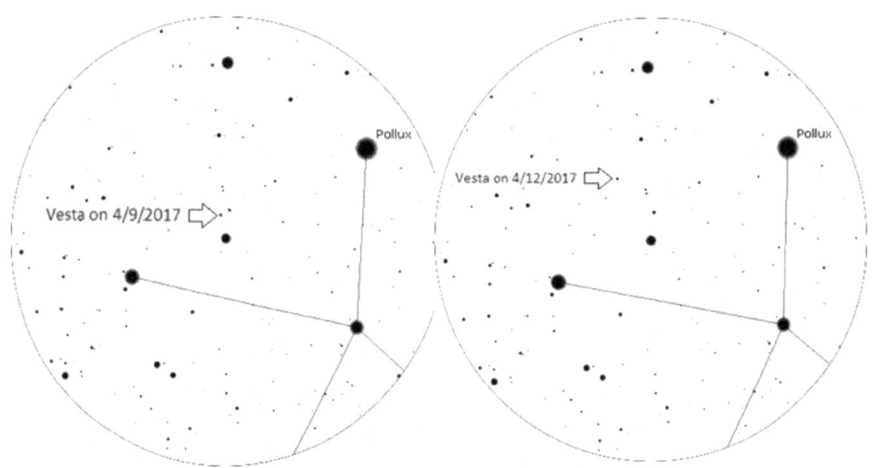

Vesta moving from one night to the next

Difficulty: ✪✪✪✪

42. Comets

What's the best way to find out if you can see a comet? Read the news. Approaching comets usually get picked up by the media. However, in the media, vastly exaggerated claims of brightness (or apocalyptic close encounters with Earth) are common. Despite the hype, only a few of these comets can actually be glimpsed by the casual sky watcher.

Comets are city-sized balls of ice, often traveling over one hundred thousand kilometers per hour. When passing in the vicinity of the Sun, comets "out-gas", creating a visible tail of particles millions of miles long.

We observe comets from a distance of hundreds of millions of miles. Though they are traveling at great speed, they are often visible for as long as a month. This gives the amateur astronomer plenty of time to observe.

Astronomy websites, and even the media, will usually report when a comet is visible in the night sky. Most of these sources will provide instructions on where to look. You may want to use binoculars to scan the sky according to the map or astronomy software. Once you have found it, move to your telescope for a closer look.

Comet through a telescope

Comet with the unaided eye

Difficulty: ✩✩✩✩

43. Star-Moon Occultation

Solar System Objects and Events

Occultations occur when one object goes behind another, in space. Sort of like an eclipse. The most common occultations are when the Moon passes in front of a bright star.

Grazing occultations tend to be the most interesting. This is when a star appears to graze the surface of the Moon, from your location. During a grazing occultation, it's not uncommon for the star to blink in and out of sight as it goes between mountain ranges or gullies on the surface of the Moon.

This is a great chance to use the "time" feature of your astronomy software. To find out when an occultation will occur (without consulting astronomical journals, magazines, or websites), just open your astronomy software and select the Moon.

After the moon has been selected, hit spacebar (if you are using "Stellarium") and lock it to the center of your screen. Using the "time" feature, begin to run the "hours" into the future. You should see the stars moving in the background, while the moon stays in place. You may have to fast forward for a few weeks before the moon occults a bright star. When it does, mark your calendar and set a reminder to watch a star disappear behind the Moon.

Alternatively, detailed annual schedules for bright star occultations, planetary occulations (detailed in the next section), and many other astronomical events, are found in the *Royal Astronomical Society of Canada Observer's Handbook*. If you are interested, the handbook can be ordered directly from the RASC website.[1]

[1] RASC Observer's Handbook (Updated Annually) https://www.rasc.ca/handbook

Difficulty: ☼☼☼☼

44. Planet-Moon Occultation

As mentioned in the previous section, an occultation occurs whenever two objects align so that one is covering the other, from the perspective of the observer. For example, if Saturn passes behind the Moon, you would say, "Saturn has been occulted by the Moon" (almost sounds like it should be a crime).

To find a planetary occultation, use the same technique as used for star occultations. Alternatively, determine the next occultation from the internet, or the *RASC Observer's Handbook.*

A planet-Moon occultation is only visible from certain locations on Earth. In the image on the right, the occultation between Mars and the Moon occurred several thousand miles south of my location. In this case, I was only able to observe a close encounter.

With a phone adapter, photographing an occultation isn't difficult, through setting the focus can take practice (generally you tap on the Moon to set the focus and exposure). If you get a good photo, post it on www.spaceweather.com. By posting it there, your photo may end up on CNN, or other major news networks!

iPhone photo of Mars and the Moon July 5th, 2014

Jupiter-Moon post-occultation (Image Simulated using Stellarium)

Difficulty: ✪✪✪✪✪

Part Five

Targets On and Near Earth

Amateur astronomers spend a lot of time with their telescopes, and not only at night. Generally, an astronomer arrives at the observing site a few hours before sunset, to set up and makes sure the equipment is ready to go. Then it's a waiting game; stargazers socialize, or play guitar, until the first stars and planets come into view. However, if you're like me, you can't wait to get started, and begin using your telescope even before it gets dark!

I've observed birds, airplanes, and distant mountains through my telescope as I've waited for darkness. I later used the techniques for observing airplanes to photograph the International Space Station.

Sometimes, I'll be observing a nebula or star cluster, when a satellite passes through my field of view. If I'm using my Dobsonian telescope (which sits on a Lazy Susan, making it extremely easy to aim), I'll leave the nebula behind and chase the satellite across the sky.

My brother-in-law's 8 inch Newtonian telescope at Glacier Point in Yosemite National Park

45. Meteor, Meteorite, Meteoroid

Meteor, Meteorite, and Meteoroid! Even I get these terms confused. A meteoroid is the term for a small rock from space. Once the rock enters the atmosphere, the light you see is a meteor, or "shooting star". To remember this, note that we say "meteor showers", and not "meteoroid showers". A space-rock is only called a meteorite once it reaches the ground. You'll probably never see a meteor**oid** in a telescope because of their size. Rocks larger than a few meters wide would be called asteroids.

If you do any amount of stargazing, you will see plenty of meteors. Just last week I was working with a science class, when a bright meteor appeared in the part of the sky we were watching. The dazzling meteor broke up and fizzled like a firework, lasting several seconds.

Author holding a meteorite

Most meteors are smaller than a golf ball, but you can see them because they move at tens of kilometers per second. When they hit the atmosphere, they generate enough heat to burn up in a bright flair.

You'll even see meteors in your telescope! With enough time spent observing, you're bound to see one cross your field of view.

Time-lapse image of Perseid meteors ***Credits: NASA/JPL***

46. Cityscapes and Landscapes

Pointing the telescope at ground-based objects is a great way to learn its power. I was volunteering at an event on Mount Diablo, in California, when we pointed the telescope toward San Francisco. The Giants had just won their game, and fireworks were going off above the stadium. You couldn't see this without the telescope, so all the kids that night gathered around and took turns watching the fireworks.

The challenge with looking at ground-based objects is that most telescopes invert the image. For this reason, some telescopes use an "inverting" lens to turn things right side up.

Landscapes become great telescope targets. This is why many tourist attractions have permanently mounted telescopes or binoculars at every lookout.

If you are at Yosemite, check out the climbers scaling El Capitan. If you are camping at the Lava Beds National Monument, check out miles and miles of volcanic rock. Camping on the beach? Use your telescope to observe the ships out at sea.

Golden Gate Bridge from Mount Diablo.
Author's Photo

Sierra Nevada Mountains from Mount Diablo.
Author's Photo

Difficulty: ☼

47. Birds

Personally, I don't know much about birds, but some folks purchase their telescopes with bird watching in mind. Some small telescopes, like the Meade ETX 60, come with a separate camera slot for this purpose.

One of the great things about viewing birds with a telescope is the depth of field. Depth of field is a term used in photography to describe the degree to which the subject is in focus. When viewing a bird on a tree with a telescope, only the bird will be in focus. This is because the telescope naturally creates a "shallow" depth of field.

Telescopes are best for viewing birds that are far away. For birds that are close, it is better to use binoculars. According to the internet, the best birds to look at through a telescope are wildfowl in the open country, or seabirds.

I captured the images below using a three hundred millimeter lens. This focal length is very similar to many small telescopes and binoculars.

48. Satellites and Satellite Flares

A normal satellite in orbit, when viewed from Earth, is about as bright as a dim star. Satellites can be observed (without a telescope) moving quickly across the sky shortly after sunset, or before sunrise. However, if that satellite is an Iridium Communications satellite, with shiny antennas, then you might be in for a treat!

The easiest way to spot the flares from Iridium Communications satellites is by downloading a phone app such as Sputnik: http://sputnikapp.info. The app creates a forecast for your location and sends you alerts when there is about to be a flare (unfortunately, the Iridium satellites will soon be deorbited, and their bright flares will cease).

You do not need a telescope to see these flares, but it may be fun to use a telescope anyway. Viewing moving objects in space is good practice for when you want to view something more challenging, like the International Space Station.

Iridium flare over San Francisco. Author's Photo.

Difficulty: ☼☼☼

49. Helicopters and Jet Aircraft

Do you live in a high crime area? I sure do. The next time the police are searching for the culprit, use your telescope to see if you can differentiate the police chopper from the news chopper.

You might think that this item is strange to be included in an astronomy book, however, the world's greatest astrophotographers, such as Thierry Legault, use aircraft as practice in preparation for spotting fast moving objects in space, such as the International Space Station. Thierry's amazing work can be found here: http://legault.perso.sfr.fr/.

To see a plane in your telescope, you'll want to use the minimum amount of magnification; this will require the use of your largest eyepiece. Use the finder scope to narrow in on the plane, and begin to move your scope to keep it in view. Keep tracking as you move from the finder scope to the eyepiece.

Tracking an aircraft is easier, or harder, depending on the type of mount you are using. A Lazy-Susan mount (called a Dobsonian), or alt-azimuth mount, will be easier, whereas an equatorial mount will be difficult, as movement is restricted.

Chasing jet aircraft is a great star party activity for children, before it gets dark. Just make sure the Sun has set, so you don't accidently point the scope in that direction. When I work with students, we sometimes play a game to see who can guess which airline the plane belongs to. Then, we look in the telescope to find out!

Space Shuttle Endeavour and carrier aircraft. Photo by Author (taken using a cell phone pressed up against binoculars)

Difficulty: ☼☼☼

50. International Space Station

Dubbed "ISS" by those in the space community, the International Space Station can be seen at least a few times per week, from almost every location on Earth. It is visible either in the morning before sunrise, or in the evening shortly after sunset.

Viewing the Space Station with your telescope can be tough, especially if you have an equatorial mount, but with a Dobsonian or tabletop design, it can be a relatively easy target. Search the internet, or use the NASA app, to determine when the International Space Station will pass over your location.

To see the ISS in your scope, use an eyepiece that provides medium magnification. Track the station in your finder (ideally a red dot finder or Telrad; one that doesn't magnify the image) and then switch to the eyepiece. If you are lucky, you may be able to make out the solar panels.

With a DSLR (digital camera) adapted to your telescope, it's possible to see much more detail, since you're able to zoom into the image (I used an exposure of 1600 and 6400 ISO to get the images below). How is it possible to see so much detail? The ISS is orbiting only a few hundred miles above the Earth, and is the size of a football field. This means the Station can appear three times as large as Saturn!

Acquiring the ISS in your scope is much easier with two people, one to track the space station in the finder scope, and one person to observe the station with the eyepiece.

ISS through a telescope
(Note: the ISS moves VERY fast)

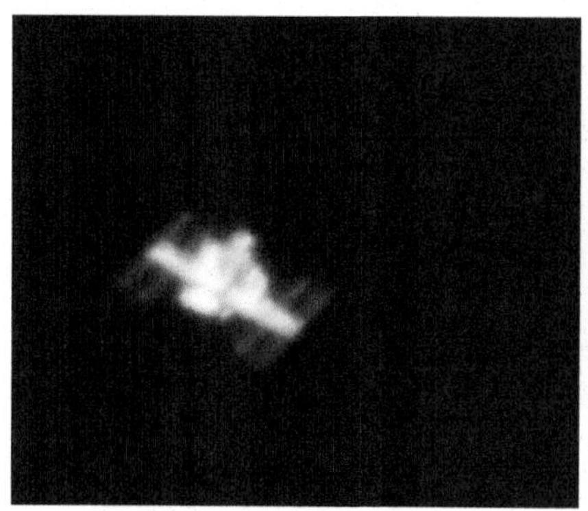

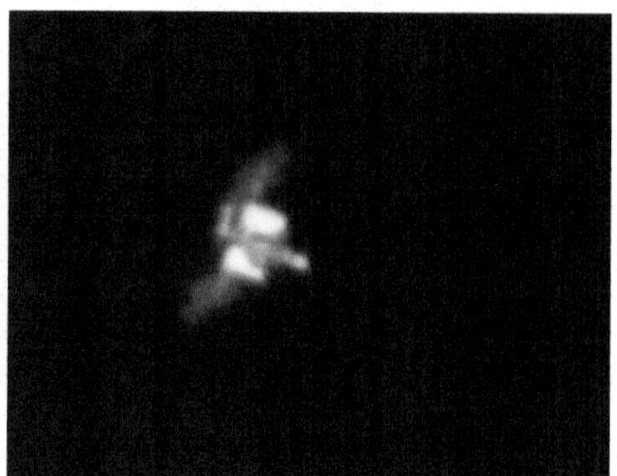

ISS. Author's Photos

Difficulty: ✩✩✩✩✩

I hope you've enjoyed this tour of 50 Things to See with a Small Telescope! If I've accomplished what I laid out in the introduction, your telescope will never see the back of a closet, or the bottom of a cellar (my telescope has a prominent place in our living room).

If you loved this book, please consider the sequel, *50 Targets for the Mid-Sized Telescope.* This full color edition features 50 new targets, organized by season, so that you'll always have plenty of things to explore during any stargazing excursion.

Appendix 1: Winter Constellation Map for the Northern Hemisphere*

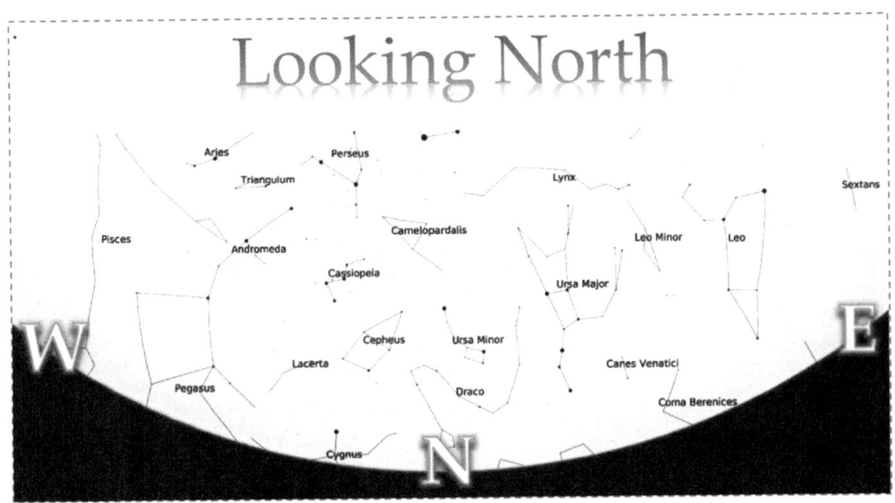

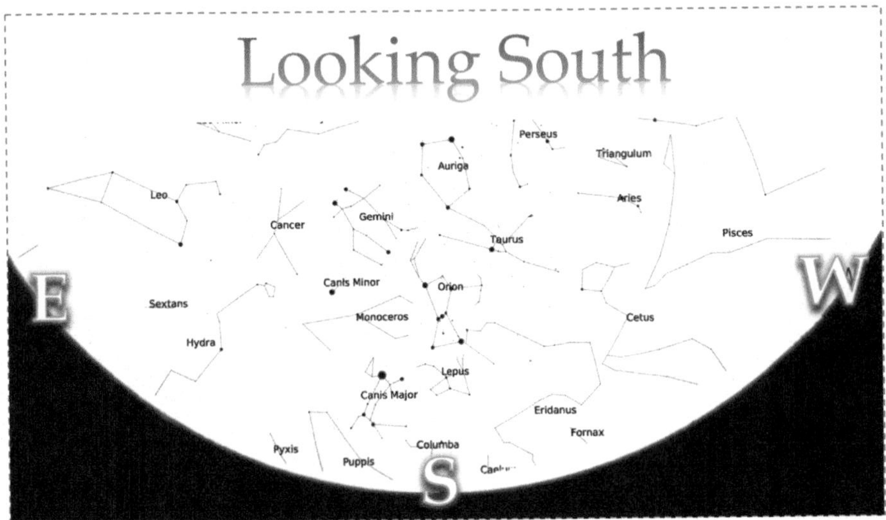

*Evening Sky - Latitude ~ 40 degrees

Appendix 2: Spring Constellation Map for the Northern Hemisphere*

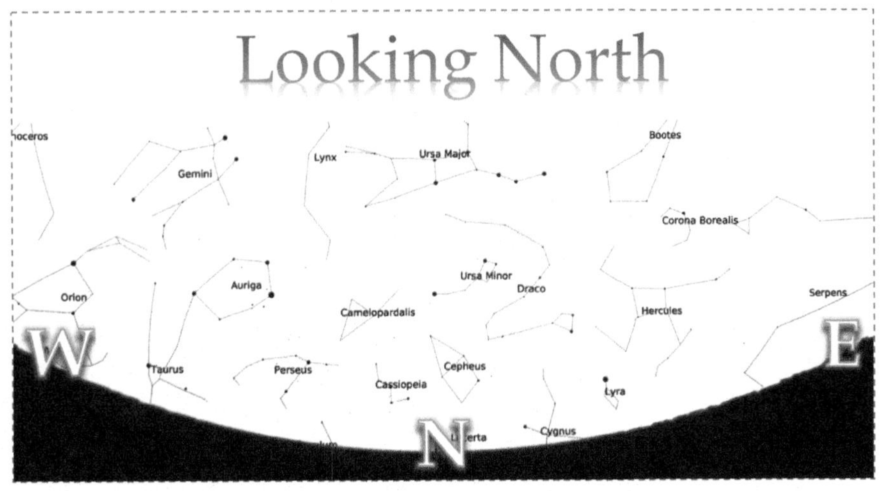

*Evening Sky - Latitude ~ 40 degrees

Appendix 3: Summer Constellation Map for the Northern Hemisphere*

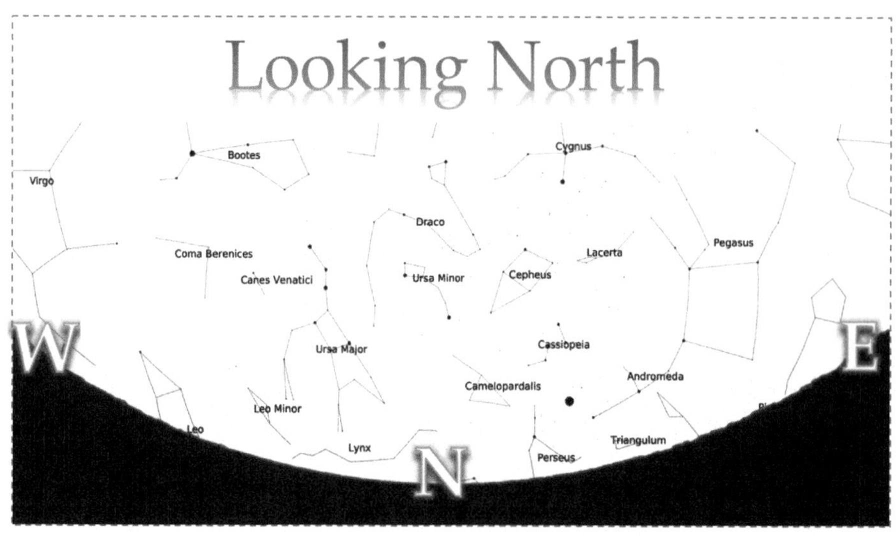

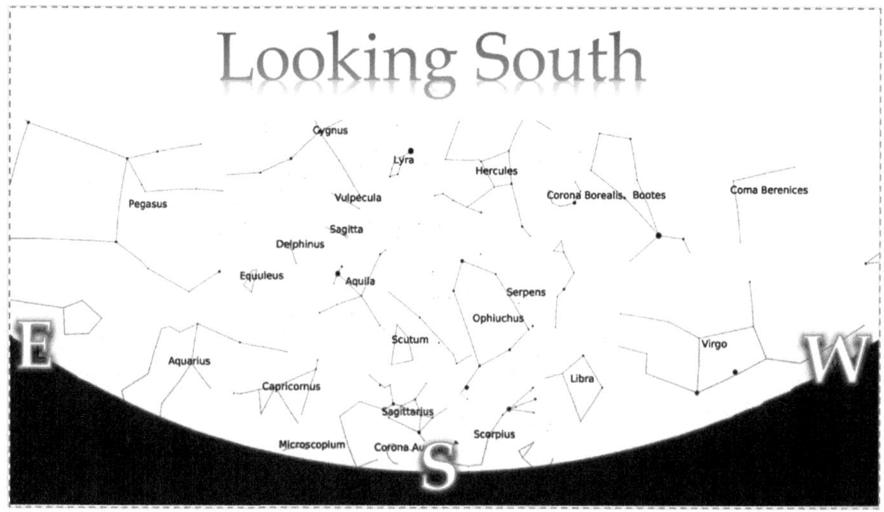

*Evening Sky - Latitude ~ 40 degrees

Appendix 4: Autumn Constellation Map for the Northern Hemisphere*

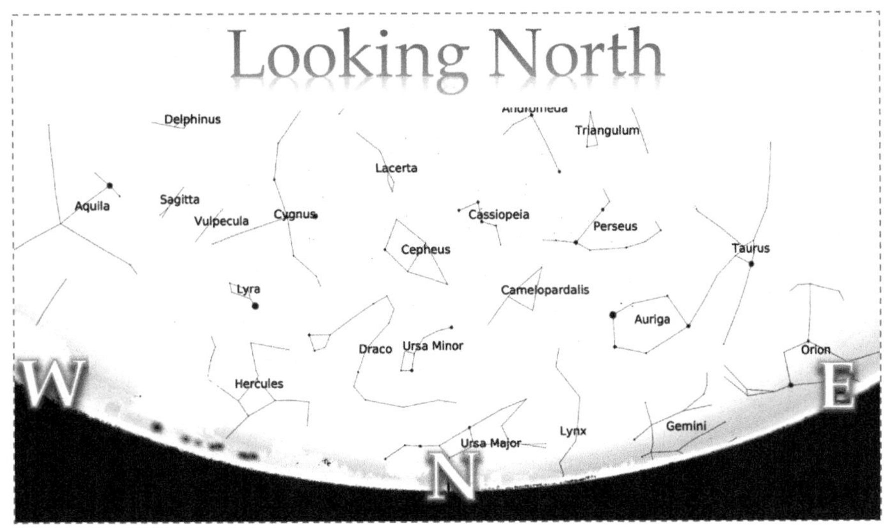

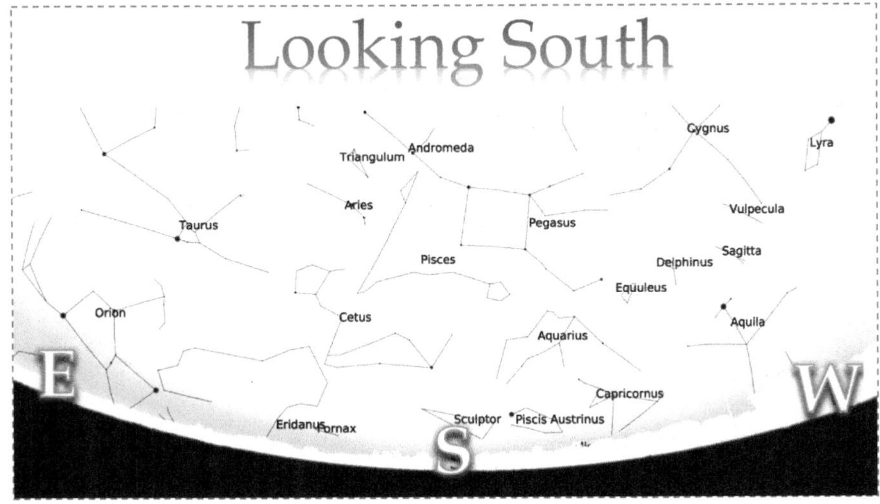

*Evening Sky - Latitude ~ 40 degrees

Appendix 5: Solar Eclipses 2016 – 2021

Type	Date	Time of Greatest Eclipse (UTC)	Location
Total	March 9, 2016	1:58:19	**Total:** Indonesia, Micronesia,Marshall Islands **Partial:** Southeastern Asia, Korea, Japan, Eastern Russia, Alaska, Northwestern Australia, Hawaii,Pacific
Annular	September 1, 2016	9:08:02	**Annular:** Atlantic, Central Africa,Madagascar, Indian Partial: Africa, Indian Ocean
Annular	February 26, 2017	14:54:33	**Annular:** southern Chile and Argentina, Angola, southwestern Katanga Partial: Southern and Western Africa, Southern South America,Antarctica
Total	August 21, 2017	18:26:40	**Total:** Oregon, Idaho, Wyoming,Nebraska, Northeastern Kansas,Missouri, southern Illinois, Western Kentucky, Tennessee, Southwestern North Carolina, Northeastern Georgia, South Carolina **Partial:** North America, Hawaii,Greenland, Iceland, British Isles, Portugal, Central America,Caribbean, northern South America, Chukchi Peninsula
Partial	February 15, 2018	20:52:33	**Partial:** Antarctica, Southern South America
Partial	July 13, 2018	3:02:16	**Partial:** South Australia, Victoria,Tasmania, Indian Ocean, Budd Coast
Partial	August 11, 2018	9:47:28	**Partial:** Northeastern Canada,Greenland, Iceland, Arctic Ocean,Scandinavia, northern British Isles, Russia, Northern Asia
Partial	January 6, 2019	1:42:38	**Partial:** Northeastern Asia, Southwestern Alaska, Aleutian Islands
Total	July 2, 2019	19:24:08	**Total:** central Argentina andChile, Tuamotu Archipelago **Partial:** South America, Easter Island, Galapagos Islands, Southern Central America,Polynesia
Annular	December 26, 2019	5:18:53	**Annular:** northeastern Saudi Arabia, Bahrain, Qatar, United Arab Emirates, Oman,Lakshadweep, Southern India, Sri Lanka, Northern Sumatra, southern Malaysia, Singapore,Borneo, central Indonesia, Palau,Micronesia, Guam **Partial:** Asia, Western Melanesia, Northwestern Australia, Middle East, East Africa
Annular	June 21, 2020	6:41:15	**Annular:** Democratic Republic of the Congo, Sudan, Ethiopia,Eritrea, Yemen, Empty Quarter,Oman, southern Pakistan, Northern India, New Delhi, Tibet, southern China, Chongqing,Taiwan **Partial:** Asia, Southeastern Europe, Africa, Middle East, WestMelanesia, Western Australia,Northern Territory, Cape York Peninsula
Total	December 14, 2020	16:14:39	**Total:** Southern Chile andArgentina, Kiribati, Polynesia **Partial:** Central and SouthernSouth America, Southwest Africa,Antarctic Peninsula, Ellsworth Land, Western Queen Maud Land
Annular	June 10, 2021	10:43:07	**Annular:** Northern Canada,Greenland, Russia **Partial:** Northern North America,Europe, Asia
Total	December 4, 2021	7:34:38	**Total:** Antarctica **Partial:** South Africa, South Atlantic
Eclipse Predictions by Fred Espenak, NASA's GSFC			

Appendix 6: Solar Eclipses 2022 - 2030

Type	Date	Time of Greatest Eclipse (UTC)	Location
Partial	April 30, 2022	20:42:36	**Partial:** Southeast Pacific, Southern South America
Partial	October 25, 2022	11:01:20	**Partial:** Europe, Northeast Africa,Mid East, West Asia
Hybrid	April 20, 2023	4:17:56	**Hybrid:** Indonesia, Australia,Papua New Guinea **Partial:** Southeast Asia, East Indies, Philippines, New Zealand
Annular	October 14, 2023	18:00:41	**Annular:** Western United States,Central America, Colombia, Brazil **Partial:** North America, Central America, South America
Total	April 8, 2024	18:18:29	**Total:** Mexico, Central United States, East Canada **Partial:** North America, Central America
Annular	October 2, 2024	18:46:13	**Annular:** Southern Chile, Southern Argentina **Partial:** Pacific, Southern South America
Partial	March 29, 2025	10:48:36	**Partial:** Northwest Africa, Europe, Northern Russia
Partial	September 21, 2025	19:43:04	**Partial:** South Pacific, New Zealand, Antarctica
Annular	February 17, 2026	12:13:06	Annular: Antarctica **Partial:** South Argentina, Chile,South Africa, Antarctica
Total	August 12, 2026	17:47:06	**Total:** Arctic, Greenland, Iceland,Spain, Northeastern Portugal **Partial:** Northern North America,Western Africa, Europe
Annular	February 6, 2027	16:00:48	**Annular:** Chile, Argentina, Atlantic Partial: South America,Antarctica, West and South Africa
Total	August 2, 2027	10:07:50	**Total:** Morocco, Spain, Algeria,Libya, Egypt, Saudi Arabia,Yemen, Somalia **Partial:** Africa, Europe, Mid East, West and South Asia
Annular	January 26, 2028	15:08:59	**Annular:** Ecuador, Peru, Brazil,Suriname, Spain, Portugal **Partial:** Eastern North America, Central and South America, Western Europe, Northwest Africa
Total	July 22, 2028	2:56:40	**Total:** Australia, New Zealand Partial: Southeast Asia, East Indies
Partial	January 14, 2029	17:13:48	**Partial:** North America, Central America
Partial	June 12, 2029	4:06:13	**Partial:** Arctic, Scandinavia,Alaska, Northern Asia, Northern Canada
Partial	July 11, 2029	15:37:19	**Partial:** Southern Chile, SouthernArgentina
Partial	December 5, 2029	15:03:58	**Partial:** Southern Argentina, Southern Chile, Antarctica
Annular	June 1, 2030	6:29:13	**Annular:** Algeria, Tunisia,Greece, Turkey, Russia, Northern China, Japan **Partial:** Europe, Northern Africa,Mid East, Asia, Arctic, Alaska
Total	November 25, 2030	6:51:37	**Total:** Botswana, South Africa,Australia **Partial:** South Africa, SouthernIndian Ocean, East Indies,Australia, Antarctica
Eclipse Predictions by Fred Espenak, NASA's GSFC			

Appendix 7: Lunar Eclipse Schedule

Eclipse Type	Date	Greatest Eclipse Time (UT ~ UTC)	Eclipse Duration	Regional Visibility
Partial	August 7, 2017	18:21:38	01h55m	Europe, Africa, Asia, Australia.
Total	January 31, 2018	13:31:00	03h23m	Asia, Australia., Pacific, Western North America
Total	July 27, 2018	20:22:54	03h55m	South America, Europe, Africa, Asia, Australia.
Total	January 21, 2019	5:13:27	03h17m	Central Pacific, Americas, Europe, Africa
Partial	July 16, 2019	21:31:55	02h58m	South America, Europe, Africa, Asia, Australia.
Total	May 26, 2021	11:19:53	03h07m	East Asia, Australia, Pacific, Americas
Partial	November 19, 2021	9:04:06	03h28m	Americas, Northern Europe, East Asia, Australia, Pacific
Total	May 16, 2022	4:12:42	03h27m	Americas, Europe, Africa
Total	November 8, 2022	11:00:22	03h40m	Asia, Australia, Pacific, Americas
Partial	October 28, 2023	20:15:18	01h17m	Eastern Americas, Europe, Africa, Asia, Australia
Partial	September 18, 2024	2:45:25	01h03m	Americas, Europe, Africa
Total	March 14, 2025	6:59:56	03h38m	Pacific, Americas, Western Europe, Western Africa
Total	September 7, 2025	18:12:58	03h29m	Europe, Africa, Asia, Australia
Total	March 3, 2026	11:34:52	03h27m	East Asia, Australia, Pacific, Americas
Partial	August 28, 2026	4:14:04	03h18m	East Pacific, Americas, Europe, Africa
Partial	January 12, 2028	4:14:13	00h56m	Americas, Europe, Africa
Partial	July 6, 2028	18:20:57	02h21m	Europe, Africa, Asia, Australia
Total	December 31, 2028	16:53:15	03h29m	Europe, Africa, Asia, Australia, Pacific
Total	January 26, 2029	3:23:22	03h40m	Americas, Europe, Africa, Middle East
Total	December 20, 2029	22:43:12	03h33m	Americas, Europe, Africa, Asia
Partial	June 15, 2030	18:34:34	02h24m	Europe, Africa, Asia, Australia

Eclipse Predictions by Fred Espenak, NASA's GSFC

CPSIA information can be obtained
at www.ICGtesting.com
Printed in the USA
BVOW05*1928181017
497992BV00013B/21/P

9 780999 034613